WILLY LEY'S FOR YOUR INFORMATION

Other Books by Willy Ley

ROCKETS, MISSILES AND SPACE TRAVEL

THE CONQUEST OF SPACE

ENGINEERS' DREAMS

WILLY LEY'S EXOTIC ZOOLOGY

WATCHERS OF THE SKIES

BEYOND THE SOLAR SYSTEM

THE EXPLORATION OF MARS (*with Wernher von Braun*)

SATELLITES, ROCKETS AND OUTER SPACE

MISSILES, MOONPROBES AND MEGAPARSECS

WILLY LEY'S
FOR YOUR INFORMATION

on Earth and in the Sky

1967, DOUBLEDAY & COMPANY, INC., GARDEN CITY, NEW YORK

INTRODUCTION

IT WOULD TAKE AT LEAST one full book to write an introduction to a book about Willy Ley. My first meeting with Willy was in 1951, when I acquired the then one-year-old *Galaxy Science Fiction Magazine*. It seemed impossible to me that any one man could have so thorough a knowledge of as many subjects as Willy displayed. Then I learned his secret: He had been everywhere and done everything and yet remains an intense student with unusual retentive power.

Our first contract with Willy for his column *For Your Information* marked the beginning of a relationship which has been both highly pleasurable—I hope for both of us—and highly educational, at least for me. In those days we were competing for Willy Ley's services not only with other publishers but with certain other bidders as well; that first contract carried a termination clause providing for cancellation "if and when Willy Ley is assigned the job of placing a space station in orbit by the United States Government." Fortunately for us, other rocket experts appeared for that sort of work and we have been lucky enough to have Willy Ley's column in every issue of *Galaxy* since.

But let's talk about Willy Ley himself. His first step into writing was in 1926, when he wrote a sixty-four-page paperback entitled *A Trip Into Space*, the first of many books

ranging in subjects from *Rockets, Missiles and Space Travel* through *Exotic Zoology.*

Willy was born October 2, 1906 in Berlin, where he received his primary and high school education. He attended the Universities of Berlin and Königsberg and received an Honorary Doctorate from Adelphi University in 1960. He was one of the original members of the German Rocket Society formed on June 5, 1927 in Breslau, Germany. The Society was formed under the name of the Society for Space Travel and is largely responsible for the rapid advancement of rocketry throughout the world. (Another member was a young man named Wernher von Braun.) He was made Director of Rocketry for the International Scientific Association for their publication called *Cosmology* and also contributed to the *Bulletin of the American Interplanetary Society.*

Willy resigned from the Society for Space Travel in 1933 when he became concerned about the frightening implications of the Nazis' assumption of power and of their taking over the affairs of the Rocket Society. On January 7, 1935, Willy Ley left Germany, then came to America via England. Since his arrival in America his books, articles and lecture tours have only emphasized his right to the title of "Mr. Authority" of the sciences.

This book, *For Your Information,* is the first of a series from our collection of his famous articles published in *Galaxy* magazine. We hope it gives you as many hours of entertainment, enlightenment and insight as it has given us!

Robert M. Guinn, Publisher
Galaxy Publishing Corporation

CONTENTS

WILLY LEY'S FOR YOUR INFORMATION

CHAPTER I

TRIBES OF THE DINOSAURS

ONE SUNNY AFTERNOON IN 1964, while standing among the replicas of dinosaurs at the New York World's Fair, I suddenly remembered a remark I had overheard several years earlier while standing among the *skeletons* of dinosaurs in the American Museum of Natural History. A man who was showing three children around told them in a loud voice and with a ring of authority that these "dinosaurs were nature's biggest failure."

Since they are now extinct the remark seemed uncontradictory but I quietly added a few figures in my mind. The so-called Age of Reptiles, during which the dinosaurs flourished, comprises the three geological periods of the Triassic, the Jurassic and the Cretaceous. The Triassic and the Jurassic each had a duration of about 35 million years, while the Cretaceous lasted 65 million years. This adds up to 135 million years, and one should really start counting a few million years prior to the Triassic which makes the time during which these "failures" flourished 140 million years.

But it is not my purpose to engage in a discussion just what constitutes a "failure." Instead, I intend to discuss the question of what the dinosaurs really were, since the term is used rather carelessly in newspaper stories, magazine articles and the movies. To begin with the word itself, it was coined

using the two Greek words, *deinos* (meaning terrible, mighty or powerful), and *sauros*, which just means lizard.

The next statement to be made is one that should be obvious, but I have found that it isn't—namely, that not every reptile is a dinosaur, even though all dinosaurs were reptiles. Reptiles are vertebrate animals which have a dry skin, often scaly, breathe by means of lungs, propagate by laying eggs, and lack a heat-regulating mechanism, so that the temperature of their blood is more or less the same as the temperature of the surrounding air or water.

A crocodile is a reptile. So are a lizard, a tortoise and a snake. But even the largest crocodile, or the fiercest-looking iguana, is not "an offspring of the dinosaurs." You might as well say that an especially large bull is "an offspring of the elephants"—both these statements are equally silly.

Nor is the mere fact that a reptile is now extinct a criterion. The eight reptilian forms pictured here are absolutely, completely and hopelessly extinct, but half of them are not dinosaurs. They are all reptiles, though, even though the word "reptile" comes from the Latin *repto*, which means "to crawl."

The reptiles got their start way back in the Permian Period, a little over 200 million years ago. The Earth was not precisely "young" any more then; endless periods had already gone by since its formation. There had been at least 2000 million years during which the planet was lifeless, then another 2000 million years when any life that existed was most likely single-celled, and another 600–700 million years with very primitive marine life, of which we know almost nothing, since they left so few fossils.

Only after all this time had passed did paleontological history begin with the Cambrian Period, which opened the so-called Paleozoic Era. That era began about 550 million

years ago and lasted through half a dozen geological periods, with a total duration of 350 million years.

Those half-dozen periods were the Cambrian, then the Ordovician, then the Silurian (the oldest known fishes belong to this period), followed by the Devonian and by the Carboniferous, a period of maximum activity with enormous forests which produced our coal, and with the earliest known insects and salamanderlike amphibians.

The last of the geological periods of the Paleozoic Era was the Permian, which produced the earliest known reptiles. They are known from Texas, from Saxony, from Russia (the Permian Period received its name from the Russian district Perm) and especially from South Africa.

The one that is considered to be the grandfather of all the reptiles was found in Texas and named Seymouria. It must have looked like a big ill-tempered salamander with long teeth. In fact, Seymouria was not a "complete" reptile yet, but is perfectly intermediate between the early amphibians which came before and the reptiles which were still to come.

The Seymouria group, also called seymouriamorphs, was, in turn, a sub-group of a larger group called the cotylosaurs, or, in English, the stem reptiles. Everything that followed began with them.

Among their earliest offshoots was a group that goes under the technical name of the therapsids, which quickly produced rather large plant-eating forms. One of the best-known of them is Moschops—the name means calf's head and don't ask me why; I can't see any similarity—from the Permian of South Africa (Fig. 1). The clumsy reptile was six feet long and must have been quite heavy. There were others that were even larger and their pictures are occasionally printed with the caption "early dinosaurs," but they were not dinosaurs yet.

FIG. 1. *Moschops capensis*, from the Permian of South Africa.

Out of this general muddle of interrelated large and clumsy, small and agile, or even large but agile primitive reptiles sprang a number of branches that were to be fruitful, hence important.

One of them, called the theriodonts (which translates as mammal teeth) actually did produce the mammals in the very next geological period, the Triassic.

Another one moved in direct strides toward the later chelonians, which is the term used by zoologists when they wish to encompass both the turtles and the tortoises.

Still another one goes under the name of thecodonts. The name is compounded of the words for tooth and for box, the reason being that their teeth had roots in separate holes in the jaws, an arrangement we tend to consider the norm, but which was by no means the norm then.

This "order" of the thecodonts had two sub-orders, called parasuchia and pseudosuchia. Translated, this gives us near-crocodiles and pseudo-crocodiles—of all things, the *Egyptian* name for crocodile is hidden in these terms—but one should

NOTE. All illustrations in this chapter have been drawn by Olga Ley.

not translate here, for they were not related to the crocodiles, which are a branch of their own.

The parasuchians at least looked somewhat like crocodiles, but the pseudosuchians were a bunch of radical innovators. Some started to climb trees, others ran on their hindlegs only, still others alternated between bipedal and quadrupedal walk. Some were armored and others were not.

In time, one sub-branch of the versatile pseudosuchians evolved into the flying reptiles of the Jurassic and Cretaceous Periods—the pterosaurs, to use their technical name. Another sub-branch of the pseudosuchians—*not* the same—learned to fly, too, by changing its scales into feathers and became the birds. And further sub-branches evolved into the dinosaurs.

A real "early dinosaur" is Plateosaurus (Fig. 2), of which

FIG. 2. *Plateosaurus longiceps*, from the Triassic of Germany.

fine specimens have been found in Germany, where Plateosaurus apparently had to migrate across a desert area every year, with a few falling by the wayside and some of them becoming fossilized.

Unfortunately the German deposits have yielded fine skeletons but no footprints. The reason this is regrettable is that we do know footprints from Connecticut which could have been made by Plateosaurus or a closely related form. But in Connecticut, no bones have been found.

Though it had not yet attained the impressive dimensions of later dinosaurs, Plateosaurus was quite big. The length of the tail alone was about eight feet.

When paleontology was a relatively young science, it seemed for a while as if all the dinosaurs should or could be sorted into two orders which could be told apart with half a glance, one walking on all fours, while the other strutted around on its hindlegs. I am sorry to report things aren't that simple.

There are two orders of dinosaurs, all right, but the distinguishing mark is not whether they walked on two or four legs. The distinguishing mark is the shape of the pelvis.

Very many of them have a pelvis which reminds anatomists of the pelvis of birds. They are the Order of the Ornithischia and are sometimes, for simplicity's sake, referred to as the

FIG. 3. *Triceratops horridus*, from the late Cretaceous of Wyoming.

"birdlike" dinosaurs. This just proves again that we should not translate scientific terms, for one of these "birdlike" dinosaurs is the rhinoceroslike—but bigger—Triceratops (Fig. 3).

On the other hand, little Compsognathus (Fig. 4) which did not quite reach the dimensions of a domestic cat, is not one of the "birdlike" dinosaurs. It belongs to the other order, the one which has a pelvis like a reptile, the Order of the Saurischia.

Now *inside* the Order of the Saurischia, the old distinction into quadrupeds and bipeds *does* hold true. The bipeds are officially the Sub-order Theropoda, and Compsognathus is one of them. So is the flesh-eating Allosaurus of the North American Jurassic and so is Tyrannosaurus of the North American Cretaceous.

Fig. 4. *Compsognathus longipes*, from the lithographic slate (late Jurassic) of South Germany.

The second sub-order of the Saurischia is the Sub-order
Sauropoda, and they are what the layman usually thinks of
when the word dinosaur is mentioned. Brontosaurus was one
of them and so was Diplodocus, both from the North American Jurassic. Another member was Brachiosaurus of eastern
Africa, which was probably the biggest of the lot, and finally
the somewhat more recent Helotus from China (Fig. 5),

FIG. 5. *Helotus zdanski,* from the early Cretaceous of Meng-Yin-
Sien in China.

which was not at all small itself, measuring some sixty-five feet
from nostrils to tail tip. The reason Helotus is pictured graz-
ing at the bottom of a lake is simply that its remains were
found in fresh-water deposits.

We now know, because of footprints found in Texas, that

the very large sauropod saurischians could walk on dry land. This is a point worth making since, for quite a number of years, it was thought that the legs of the sauropods, while massive, could support the body only if shallow water helped them to carry it. They probably did not go hiking for fun, but if they had to cross dry land to get from one lake to another, they could.

As I said, the old distinction of bipeds on the one hand and quadrupeds on the other hand can still be made, provided you stay inside the Order of the Saurischia. In the other order of the true dinosaurs, the Ornithischia, you can do the same, except for one main difference. The quadrupeds belonging to the Order Ornithischia are so different from each other that they form separate sub-orders.

Let's look at this in a little more detail. The first sub-order of the Ornithischia is that of the Ornithopoda (bird-footed). In the Jurassic Period, this sub-order was represented by the bipedal dinosaur Camptosaurus, which hasn't received much publicity in other than professional books. But the ornithopods of the Cretaceous are well known; they are the so-called duck-billed dinosaurs, of which Trachodon is the favorite example.

The remaining three sub-orders of the Ornithischia are all quadrupeds and they are called Stegosauria, Ankylosauria and Ceratopsia.

The first of these three is represented, of course, by the well-known stegosaur, which bore a crest of enormous triangular bony plates on its back, with a few paired sets of spikes on the tail to make the defensive armament complete.

The name stegosaur is based on the Greek word for roof— apparently the first discoverer thought that the triangular plates were lying flat on the body as armor, giving the effect of shingles. We now know that they did not and it probably

was the weight of these plates which made stegosaur into a quadruped. The study of his anatomical features makes it perfectly clear that this type was bipedal and readapted to walking on all four legs only after it had already acquired the features that go with a usually upright position.

The next sub-order, that of the Ankylosauria, is not too well known to the public and the main representative Ankylosaurus is not very easy to describe. The difficulty begins with the name, for the Greek word *ankylos* can mean curved or crooked or else stiff-jointed. Both meanings apply, the curved to its ribs, the stiff-jointed to its general appearance. It has been called the "tank of the Cretaceous Period," squat and heavy in build, with a broad armor-plated skull, a heavy stiff tail with a clublike bone at the tip, and, for all we know, with horny spikes along the sides.

The last sub-order of the Ornithischia was also massive in build and heavily armored, at least in front. They were the Ceratopsia (Fig. 3).

And there you have the tribes of the dinosaurs, all six of them: the Theropoda (example: Tyrannosaurus), the Sauropoda (example: Brontosaurus), the Ornithopoda (example: Trachodon, the duck-bill), the Stegosauria, the Ankylosauria and the Ceratopsia. There weren't any others when the dinosaurs were at their peak.

But how about things like the plesiosaurs in the sea, the flying saurians in the air?

They were reptiles and can be called saurians, but they were not dinosaurs. The ones usually called plesiosaurs form a reptilian order of their own, the Order Sauropterygia. These long-necked "sea serpents" with their four paddles became more long-necked as time went on. The plesiosaurus of the Jurassic Period was already giraffe-necked. What happened in the Cretaceous with Elasmosaurus can be seen in Fig. 6.

FIG. 6. *Elasmosaurus platyurus,* from the late Cretaceous (Niobrara Sea) of Kansas.

More numerous than the plesiosaurs were another type of marine reptiles of the general shape and size of a dolphin, the ichthyosaurs (Fig. 7). They also form a reptilian order of their own, the Order Ichthyosauria, from Greek *ichthys* for fish and *sauros* for lizard.

How well distributed they were can be told by a survey of their life history. The earliest known types of the ichthyosaurs were found mostly in California. A somewhat later type, but still from the Triassic Period, was found in Spitsbergen and named *Mixosaurus nordenskjöldi,* and another one of the same age—give or take half a million years—came to light in Nevada. The vast majority of the ichthyosaurs of the Jurassic Period, however, is concentrated in South Germany and South England.

To forestall questions as to why the ichthyosaur of Fig. 7 has a different name, I have to explain that during the Jurassic Period—more precisely, in the first of the three sub-periods of the Jurassic Period, when they were most numerous—three main types were around in quantities. They could be told apart best by the shape of their paddles (*pteryx* in Greek), which were either broad (*europs* in Greek) or else narrow (*stenops*) or slender (*leptos*). Hence the three types received the designations *Europterygius, Stenopterygius* and *Leptopterygius*.

Fig. 7. *Stenopterygius quadriscissus* (ichthyosaur) from the Lias (early Jurassic) of South Germany.

The ichthyosaurs did not continue beyond the end of the Jurassic Period and their last representatives were weak-looking and very nearly toothless types. Apparently they disappeared because they had too much competition from other marine reptiles which grew large then—with teeth to match—and from the sharks, which all of a geological sudden produced a number of formidable types.

over the Niobrara Sea that covered Kansas
states during the last part of the Cretaceous
nd of Pteranodon has led to the suspicion that
have been even more unusual than shown. It
t it had a large throat pouch for pre-digesting
ing fish. The experts, so far, only say that this
the artists hope that they won't become definite
for a dangling throat pouch under this head is
convincingly.

urse, the inevitable question will come up why
nding forms became extinct at the end of the
riod. There is no simple answer to this question
was no single cause for the extinction of the
d those other reptile tribes.

this around first and see what is left of the Class
lia. The following is a listing of all the orders—
I have the choice of either following the system
rofessor Othenio Abel of Vienna University, or
essor Baron von Huene of Tübingen University,
ofessor Alfred Sherwood Romer of Harvard Uni-
I have decided in favor of Harvard—with notes
o their fates.

YLOSAURIA, the stem reptiles, extinct even be-
days of the dinosaurs.
LONIA, tortoises and turtles, still with us.
THYOSAURIA, extinct since end of the Jurassic

ROPTERYGIA, plesiosaurs, extinct since end of
us Period.
UCHIA, ancient reptiles, extinct at an early date.
NCHOCEPHALIA, another type of ancient rep-
st of them extinct at an early date, but one, Hat-
ll alive on islets near New Zealand.

Order SQUAMATA, which has two sub-orders, the LACER-
TILIA or lizards and the OPHIDIA or snakes, both still
with us; the snakes are the most recent reptilian type to
have evolved.
Order THECODONTIA, ancient reptiles, as explained, ex-
tinct.
Order CROCODILIA, crocodiles and alligators, still with us;
they don't date back past the Jurassic Period.
Order PTEROSAURIA, flying reptiles, lasted only through
Jurassic and Cretaceous.
Order SAURISCHIA, dinosaurs, two sub-orders, extinct.
Order ORNITHISCHIA, dinosaurs, four sub-orders, extinct.
Order PELYCOSAURIA, very early forms, extinct.
Order THERAPSIDA, very early and somewhat mammal-
like forms, extinct, but the mammals sprang from one of
these last two orders.

A careful reading of this list shows that the most numerous
reptiles of our time, namely crocodiles, alligators, snakes and
lizards are of comparatively recent origin. But the chelonians
(tortoises and turtles) are also still numerous though they
date back to the very beginning of the Age of Reptiles. The
chelonians, then, may be considered the most "successful"
order of the reptiles.

But what happened to those that are no longer around?
Well, the cotylosaurians, the eosuchians and the therapsida
disappeared because they evolved into something else, other
reptiles, birds and mammals. As for the spectacular forms,
like the true dinosaurs, the ichthyosaurs and the flying saurians
one can think of reasons for their extermination in a few
cases, though not for all. But it must be kept in mind that
saying "they became extinct at the end of the Cretaceous
Period" is putting it very vaguely indeed. That statement

still leaves a leeway of a few million years, and after all dinosaurs had been extinct on Continent A, they might still have been thriving on Continent B.

The reasons? A large forest fire, set by lightning, could easily wipe out a tribe of pterosaurs. The ichthyosaurs succumbed to competition after they, presumably adapting to a diet of squid, had shed their own teeth. Many tribes, especially when living on small continents or very large islands, could have been eradicated by egg-eaters. Small mammals like eggs and so do birds—and so do snakes, the last offspring of the reptiles themselves.

The large forms probably succumbed to fairly minor climatic changes, simply because they were large. Reptiles lack sweat glands and die of heat stroke if the sun is hot and no water and shade are available. A minor earthquake resulting in the draining of a few sets of large shallow lakes would indirectly kill off whole armies of sauropods. A small lizard can shade itself in underbush or in cracks between rocks; a brontosaurus could not.

Early in this century a few scientists felt that species, families and whole orders might finally succumb to collective aging and might die out just because their kind has existed for a long time. Nobody believes this anymore, there are too many life forms around that have existed even before the dinosaurs came into being. But just these "living fossils" do teach a lesson of sorts. They are usually fairly small, they are omnivorous and do not rely on a very special diet for their survival, and they seem to be fairly unaffected by climatic changes. If this is the reason for their survival we can conclude that very specialized forms, forms that need specific food plants, or a specific environment, are not likely to survive if changes occur. Most of the dinosaurs were quite specialized, but they had the good luck to live at a time when major changes of environment did not occur very often.

And the flying reptiles?

They are a separate order, too, that of the Pterosauria— that Greek word *pteryx* can mean wing as well. We do know that nimble tree-climbing pseudosuchians were their ancestors, but we can't tell just when and where they put in their first appearance. When they did show up, in European deposits from the Jurassic Period, they already came in two sharply distinguished types.

One of these, presumably the somewhat older, was the pterodactylus type, with a very short tail and usually tiny in size, ranging from about that of a sparrow to that of a pigeon or slightly larger. The other was the rhamphorhynchus type, which had a long tail with a tiny skin rudder at its tip and which tended to be somewhat larger, about like a duck. The pterodactylus type seems to have been insect eaters (some have rather large eyes, indicating nocturnal flying) while the rhamphorhynchus type probably was fish-eating.

The pterosaurs did produce one giant, Pteranodon (Fig. 8),

FIG. 8. *Pteranodon ingens,* from the late Cretaceous (Niobrara Sea) of Kansas.

CHAPTER II

THE MAN I DIDN'T MEET

EVERY ONCE IN A WHILE somebody asks me whom I would nominate as the "most fascinating man I ever met" and that is a question I cannot answer. In the first place it could be a woman—let us say Dr. Lise Meitner whom I, however, never met—and in the second place most of the people I could name are still alive and I don't know how they will develop. More important, to me at least, I am still alive—which means that I'll probably meet a few more fascinating people.

Since I cannot write about the most fascinating man I met I'll write, instead, about a (presumably) fascinating man I *almost* met. I was in High School then. I must have been about 17 years old. My teacher of French, Dr. Sepp Schneider, was a ski enthusiast . . . which has some bearing on the story. He had helped to make a feature-length movie about skiing and needed some help in distributing literature to the audience of a first private screening. I was drafted. To enhance my enthusiasm for this job he told me that he had invited Dr. Theodor Zell to be in the audience and that he would introduce me to Dr. Zell after the screening.

That was enough for me. I had been reading Dr. Zell's books for some six years and had bought all of them that were still in print. (Fortunately for my pocketbook most of them were what we now call paperbacks.)

Dr. Schneider had known Dr. Zell for many years. He

told me what was then still a secret, namely that the well-known name, "Dr. Theodor Zell," was a pen name. His real name was Dr. Leopold Bauke.

Germans are, as a rule, bitterly opposed to name changes since this implies a wilful break with family traditions. Dr. Bauke had made an exception. It so happens that his real name is the idiomatic German word (somewhat mispronounced, which produces a humorous effect) for the bass drum of an Infantry band. Such a name would not do on the cover of a zoological book. Therefore Bauke had changed it (for literary purposes only) to Zell. This corresponded, or at least hinted at, the zoological content, since the German word *Zelle* means "cell" in the biological sense. It does mean a cell in jail, too; but it was most unlikely that anybody would take that meaning for a pseudonym.

Well, Dr. Zell did not come to the movie preview. His friend Dr. Schneider promised me that he would make another appointment. It was scheduled several months later and then cancelled. Schneider remarked, "Theodor seems to be quite sick." He was. Half a year later I read about his death.

So I never actually did meet Dr. Zell.

Who was he?

The external circumstances of his life can be told in one paragraph, and even that paragraph is just for completeness' sake. He was born in 1862 on an estate some three score miles from Berlin. He studied law, presumably at his father's request, and finally received the title *Doktor beider Rechte*, or "doctor of both laws"—meaning Roman and *Code Napoléon*. Then he settled in Berlin and started writing about animals.

Within five years he was famous. Of course, a few people

attacked his views; but ten times as many defended them. Only a very few people knew him personally, though some of his books sold more than 100,000 copies. In 1924 he quietly died. His obituary did not even mention the cause of death.

There exists a joke about a man who, for the first time in his life, attends a theatrical performance, which happens to be *Hamlet*. On his way out he is heard to mutter: "All that fellow Shakespeare did was string a lot of quotations together." Something similar may be said about Dr. Zell's work. Many of the ideas are now simply taken for granted that even people old enough to know about Dr. Zell do not know that it was he who said so first. And the younger generation of zoologists doesn't even know his name.

In writing about Dr. Zell it is therefore not very important who he was. What counts is what he said. His specialty was to explain actions of animals which seem mysterious or senseless to the casual observer. Interestingly enough, he never ran an animal experiment in the modern sense. He only observed.

Some of his work dealt with stories current in his time. One of them, which I heard myself as a boy from a forester, dealt with the mixed offspring of wolves and domesticated dogs. That they do interbreed is a fact well known to every outdoorsman in the areas where wolves occur. The story was that puppies resulting from such a mixed marriage could be domesticated, but that pure wolf puppies could not. But if you found puppies in the forest, how could you tell whether they were dog, mixed or wolf?

Very simple, said the people of what is now Poland and the western fringe of Soviet Russia. You pen them up for a few hours. Then, when they are likely to be thirsty, you give them water. If they lap it up with their tongues like domestic

dogs they are dogs or mixed and can be kept. But if they drink like sheep, they are wolves and must be killed.

Nobody ever doubted that story; everybody had learned it early in life from his father. Except Dr. Zell. He had grown up with lots of dogs and had seen wolves. There was no difference in the build of the mouth; why should there be one in drinking habits? "It took one trip to the zoo," he wrote, "but then it took five hours of patience." After that time all three species of wolves had performed for him, all of them lapping the water like his own dogs.

Another problem was the one of how carrion-eating birds find their food. The customary answer was that these birds have a fantastically keen sense of smell, so keen that they not only smell a dead body miles away but that they can even smell it if a person or an animal is going to die soon. We now know that this is nonsense. Birds (with the possible exception of the New Zealand kiwi) don't have any sense of smell at all. True, the bill of most birds still shows holes where nostrils normally belong, but there is nothing behind it to do the actual smelling.

About sixty years ago a naturalist began to grow doubtful. He expressed his thoughts in the following manner: "The eye operates by means of light rays; the nose needs particles of the smelling substance to work on. A bird circling, say, five hundred yards up is likely to be above the limit to which such particles will ascend. Moreover, it is moving so fast that its nose would be handicapped by its very speed. Therefore I believe that, in the case of birds, the sense of smell plays a very minor rôle in the process of locating food."

Dr. Zell went one step farther. With numerous examples he showed that in the case of birds the sense of smell plays no rôle at all. (This was before the anatomical impossibility

of a bird smelling anything had been demonstrated.) When
he declared categorically, "Birds go by sight only," he had
already postulated his main theory, namely the distinction of
animals into "eye-guided" and "nose-guided."

Just to avoid misunderstandings I have to point out that
Dr. Zell (though he mentioned insects occasionally) was
essentially concerned with mammals and birds. Since it turned
out that all birds are exclusively "eye-guided," the discussion
of animal behavior dealt with mammals, especially with domesticated animals and game.

He related at one time that the casual question of why
some dogs bay at the moon started him thinking. Another
thing that stuck in his mind was the rather unflattering German saying, "So-and-so behaved just as stupid as a cow confronted with a new door to the stable." The third example
that provided a clue to him was a story told by a lady who
owned an English bulldog. While the maid was taking the dog
for a stroll, a new and very large mirror was installed in the
lady's boudoir. As the dog was brought in and saw his reflection in the big mirror he started to growl and evidently
got ready for battle, approaching his reflection stiff-legged,
cautious and teeth ready, until he was about a yard from
the mirror. Then he sniffed a few times and quietly settled
down in his favorite corner on the carpet.

The lady concluded that her pet quieted down as soon as
he recognized himself in the mirror.

That, Dr. Zell said, was not the reason—even though he
did not doubt the facts as related. Dogs are the commonest
example of a nose-guided animal. If dogs could talk (this is
my statement, not Dr. Zell's), they would not say, "Let me
see," they would say, "Let me smell." To a dog things
do not "look right," they "smell right." And just as we may
look very carefully at something which is by no means a

pretty sight, so a dog may carefully sniff something which doesn't smell nice at all. He needs a "smell identification" to make sense out of something (or just to remember it) while we need a "picture identification" for the same reasons.

Keeping in mind that the dog is "nose-guided," the story of the bulldog and the large mirror appears in a different light. On entering the boudoir the dog saw another dog and prepared himself for a fight, just in case. As he came closer, the "other dog" came closer too. But when they were within jumping distance the bulldog could not smell the "other dog." Hence there *was* no other dog—and he might as well take a nap.

The cow that stands, seemingly the epitome of stupidity, in front of the new stable door is in a similar dilemma. Cows are "nose-guided" too. Now, all the way home all the smells are as they should be and where they should be. But just before entering the stable one expected smell (that of the old door) is missing and a new one, not at all resembling the old one (namely freshly cut wood and paint), is in its place. To a nose-guided animal this can only mean that there is something fundamentally wrong. To an eye-guided animal the difference would be minor; the door would have the right size and shape and approximately the same color as the old one.

Oh, yes, the baying at the moon.

Well, there is something up there which can be seen. It isn't there all the time, in which case one would probably learn to ignore it. But even when there it has no smell at all, which is dismaying.

As Dr. Zell phrased it: "Just try to imagine how we would feel if there was something in our room which we could smell and even feel, but could not see. It would be a rather upsetting experience!"

Since the nose is so important to the dog, their habit of leaving a "visiting card" at trees and fireplugs becomes clear too. They smell not just that another dog has been there, but *which* other dog. If you watch your own dog's behavior carefully you can almost guess it too, because one other dog is considered a friend, while another dog is the opposite. The point here is again that you have to *see* how your own dog behaves; your dog goes by his nose. Dr. Zell coined the term "the nose-guided animal's post office" for these landmarks where a "notice," (in the form of a smell) is left.[1]

The American writer Ernest Thompson-Seton had arrived at the same conclusion, incidentally. He wrote that when the wolf Lobo stuck his nose into the air and sniffed for ten minutes it was to him as if you spend ten minutes with the morning newspaper. You learn what has been going on in your absence, or while you were asleep.

Naturally Dr. Zell's distinction into nose-guided and eye-guided was not supposed to mean that the animal in question goes by this one sense only. Except the birds; it is quite possible that the old naturalist guessed right when he pointed to the high speed of movement as the cause. We are ourselves eye-guided animals. But we sniff for a gas leak (this partly due to the fact that we *know* that gas cannot be seen), and when a piece of meat which has been overlooked in the refrigerator for some time does not "look right" we make our nose a consultant. Likewise dogs do see, though apparently poorly (with the exception of some breeds like the greyhound), but to them sight is secondary. We trust our eyes. The dog trusts his nose. In passing it may be re-

---

[1] The concept of the "animal's post office" led to an explanation of the often observed fact that wolves and coyotes carry old bones, pieces of tree branches, etc., around for considerable distances. In Dr. Zell's opinion this was done to remove "superfluous" post offices so that the number of places to be inspected would not get out of hand.

marked that this explains why an old blind dog does not seem to be particularly unhappy. He is in about the position of a man who has lost his sense of smell; it's distressing on occasion, but no major catastrophe.

Mostly because some critics misconstrued "nose-guided" into "exclusively nose-guided" and other critics brought up the question "what about hearing?" Dr. Zell later phrased his guiding idea differently by saying that "among higher mammals the sum of the three major senses (sight, smell and hearing) is a constant." It seems to me that the nose-guided animals place a little more reliance on their hearing than do the eye-guided animals.

Well, that's the story of the man I didn't meet. Possibly he wouldn't have been too interesting as a person. But his ideas were—and these we can still talk about.

CHAPTER III

KING OF THE RATS

FOR THOSE WHO KNOW Tchaikovsky's *Nutcracker Ballet* only from records and have never seen it staged it may be necessary to explain that there is a Mouse King on stage. It has many heads—mouse-heads, of course—and for that reason it doesn't have much to do. But the choreographer's problems are beside the point here, as is the fact that the ballet is based on a French rewrite of a story by E. T. A. Hoffmann, he of the *Tales of Hoffmann*.

What is to the point is that the Mouse King of the ballet was a Rat King in the original story, and that there is a little known fact of Natural History hiding behind the fantasy.

Quite a number of years ago, at a Christmas party where the hostess told me that she had taken her children to see the ballet, I tried to tell that fact, but was interrupted with the remark that this was "not a nice story." I just found out that Richard Lydekker, who edited the multi-volume *Library of Natural History* which was published in New York in 1902, also did not consider it a "nice story," for while he followed his original, Dr. Alfred Brehm's *Tierleben*, quite faithfully, he left out the three pages of the original which deal with the Rat King.

A Rat King is not a separate species. One is tempted to

say "on the contrary," for it consists of a number of rats which cannot be separated.

The average number of rats forming a "king" is twelve, but larger and smaller numbers have been found. The tails of the animals are intertwined in such a manner that the individuals cannot pull free. The whole thing is about two feet in diameter. All the heads point outward, naturally, since the tails are stuck together. Being handicapped in this manner, the animals are not very mobile and in a few cases a dead and dried-out "king" has been found. Evidently the rats had starved to death. But in the majority of the cases the "king" when found was still alive. It often was found because the members composing it were squealing with hunger.

A number of writers have dismissed the Rat King as "legendary" but that seems to be due to a confusion, just as the term Rat King itself is somewhat confused—as I'll explain shortly. There is a European legend about a "king of the rats" which is old enough to be untraceable because its roots disappear in the time before printing. But the name was known to Conrad Gesner, the great Swiss zoologist of the sixteenth century. In his book on the four-footed animals, which was printed for the first time in 1551, he said in his chapter on the rat—after remarking that rats do not need to be described because "to many they are better known than is pleasing"—that "some say that the rat, in its old age, grows enormously large [so that it can no longer move around] and is fed by the younger rats; it is called a Rat King by our people."

This is a reference to the legend which other writers expanded, saying that the younger rats steal red cloth to drape on their king. Many a young Swiss probably gripped his stick more tightly when opening the door of a long unused barn or basement. There might be an enormous rat inside, im-

mobile because of age and size, maybe, but still equipped with long teeth and possibly defended by faithful retainers. Of course no Rat King of that kind was ever found, though it made fine material for fairy tales. But once in a while peasant lads would find the nearly immobile assembly of rats with their tails stuck together. Was that the Rat King's throne? Or did the king of the rats look different from the fairy tales? In the end linguistic usage decided that it was the Rat King.

Two types of rats were common in Europe. In England they are distinguished simply by the color of their fur as Black and Brown rats. The latter goes under the name of Norway Rat in some books. Zoologists know that the, incidentally larger, brown rat is a fairly late immigrant to Europe. The same is believed of the black rat, but the date of immigration was early. The first mention of the black rat can be found in the works of Albert of Bollstädt, better known as Albertus Magnus, who died in 1280. Whether they arrived, presumably from the East, a century or five centuries before Albertus is something nobody knows.

But the arrival of the brown rat has even been observed. The German physician Peter Simon Pallas, who explored Russia for the Court in St. Petersburg, reported that large numbers of brown rats could be seen traveling westward after an earthquake in the area of the Caspian Sea. The date was early autumn of 1727. The brown rat appeared in East Prussia in 1750, in Paris in 1753, in South Germany in 1780 and in Switzerland in 1809. But in the meantime brown rats from the East Indies had reached England by ship in 1732 and had traveled from England to the United States in 1755. The brown rat is considerably larger than the black rat, and more destructive in the same ratio. It was only a minor consolation that the first victims of the brown rat's appetite were usually the black rats.

Around the year 1850, the inhabitants of Denmark, Germany and Switzerland still referred to the two rats as "basement rats" and "attic rats," the smaller black rat (*Mus rattus*) preferring the roof area, while the larger brown rat (*Mus decumanus*) preferred the basements. By the end of the nineteenth century the brown rat had won out. The black rat had become rare. And the Reverend J. G. Wood, who near the end of the nineteenth century wrote a book called *Animate Creation*, was more than slightly wrong in writing that the "conquest had been brought about not by war but by love," thinking that in interbreeding the characteristics of the brown rat had become dominant. It had been war, plain and simple.

This excursion into the history of the two kinds of rats has been necessary for a specific reason. Whatever it is that causes a dozen or so rats to become a Rat King affects the black rat only, as far as we can tell from old descriptions. It does not seem to touch the brown rat. And since the black rat has become comparatively rare the chances for forming Rat Kings have diminished too. This must be the reason why there are no recent reports.

But since the majority of these reports are old how can we know that they are true? Fortunately we have the documents of the equivalent of a law suit involving a Rat King.

On January 17, 1774, a young man came to the district office of the government of the king of Saxony in Leipzig with a complaint. His name, he stated, was Christian Kaiser and he was employed as a helper at the windmill at Lindenau, a hamlet within walking distance from Leipzig. A week earlier he had found a live Rat King consisting of sixteen rats whose tails were intertwined. He had shown it to his master, the miller Tobias Jaeger. The reason why he bothered the officials was to complain about one Johann Adam Fasshauer, a resident

of Lindenau. Said Johann Adam Fasshauer had gone to the aforementioned miller Tobias Jaeger and persuaded him to hand over the Rat King to said Fasshauer because he wished to make a painting of it. But in reality Fasshauer had exhibited the Rat King, charging admission, and petitioner was now petitioning the officials to force said Fasshauer to return the Rat King, to hand over the money he had earned by its public exhibition and also to pay the expenses for the action of the officials.

Before committing themselves on the legal steps to be taken the officials made sure that there was a Rat King.

They first questioned Christian Kaiser under oath about details of the capture. He told that he was working in the mill on January 12, 1774, when he heard a noise near a staircase and saw several rats looking out at him. Taking a piece of firewood, he killed them, and then took a ladder to see whether there might be more rats on a ledge, this time taking an axe as a weapon. There he found the Rat King. He pulled it off the ledge, using the axe so that it fell to the floor. He counted sixteen rats, fifteen of them with their tails "plaited together" and the sixteenth sticking to the back fur of one of the fifteen. Most of them survived the fall from the ledge and stayed alive for some time. But though they attempted to pull free of each other they did not succeed.

The next step of the officials was to send a doctor to Lindenau. Then the doctor wrote a protocol, saying that he had arrived in Lindenau and had been led to a room in the Posthorn Inn where he had found a Rat King consisting of sixteen dead rats.

"Fifteen of them," the doctor wrote, "had their tails knotted together into a large knot in such a manner that most tails were completely in the knot except for a piece one or two

inches in length near their bodies." He then examined the
rats in detail, and summarized the result of his examination
in the following four points:

"(1) that the bodies, heads and feet of the rats had their
natural shapes,

"(2) that some of them had the color of gray ashes,
some were a little darker and some almost black,

"(3) that they measured more than a span in length
[this must refer to the length of the head and body without
the tail; the normal figure for a black rat is about seven
inches],

"(4) that the proportions of their thickness to their length
indicated that they were undernourished rather than well
nourished."

His conclusion was that "said sixteen rats were not one
organism which is called a Rat King but sixteen individual
rats of different size and coloration and (in my opinion)
different age and sex." As for the reason, he pointed out that
there had been a cold spell prior to the discovery. He thought
that the rats had huddled together for warmth but that the
urine of other rats hiding at a higher level had dripped down
on the intertwined tails and had frozen.

I am sorry that I can't report whether the officials
decided that Johann Adam Fasshauer had to return the Rat
King to Christian Kaiser along with the money he had
earned by its exhibition. Since my source is a zoological
book, the legal consequences have been neglected, but the
point is that after all these legalities and investigations the
authenticity of the fact involved cannot easily be doubted. The
good doctor's explanation of how the Rat King came into
being is admittedly weak, but we still don't know what the actual reason is. Some later investigators have offered the guess

that it might be the result of a disease of some kind which is peculiar to the black rat.

At any event, the Rat King of Lindenau was not unique.

During December, 1822, two Rat Kings were found by three farm hands engaged in threshing grain in the barn of the local forester. The place was the hamlet of Döllstedt, not quite ten miles from the city of Gotha. While doing their work, the men heard the squealing of rats and started a search, aided by the forester's helper. They finally found that one of the main cross beams had a six-inch-deep hollow in its topside, evidently one that the rats had gnawed. They saw that this hollow was full of rats, and they were somewhat surprised that the rats made no attempt to run away.

The men pushed the rats out, and saw that one was a Rat King of twenty-eight rats and the other one, one of fourteen rats. Both sets were described as consisting of fully grown rats, quite clean but also very hungry. Strangely enough they are also described as having been very docile, which probably means that the rats were in an advanced state of weakness from hunger.

After the whole village had marveled at the find, the public spectacle ended by the execution of both Rat Kings, the execution being carried out with the flails. Then two of the men took pitchforks and tried to pry the bodies of the smaller assembly apart. After much effort they succeeded in pulling out a few of the rats. The forester himself looked at them and wrote down that the tails had not been torn off in the process and even had their skin, but they "showed the impressions of the other tails, just like leather straps that had been plaited together for a long time."

A later case has the advantage of having been examined by a man with scientific knowledge. The Rat King was found on February 2, 1880 by a drayman in a room of the abattoir of

the city of Düsseldorf. It was a room which was used for the storage of skins and which was, for this reason, not much frequented by people. The Rat King consisted of eight black rats, of which one was killed when it was discovered. The other seven lived for some time. A Mr. Wilhelm Deckers acquired it and went to a taxidermist to have it preserved. The taxidermist, naturally, cleaned it up so that one cannot tell whether the intertwined tails were also held together by anything that might act like glue.

After Mr. Deckers died, the specimen was donated to the local High School and examined by the school's science teacher, Prof. Ahrend. Ahrend wrote that "Guntermann [the taxidermist] had cleaned the tails of the animals carefully so that only their intertwined positions were preserved . . . but just looking at the intertwined tails makes it clear that even the smallest amount of a sticky substance would render the animals inseparable."

The latest case which I could find in a quick survey was reported by the German zoologist Dr. Ludwig Heck, who later became the director of the Zoological Garden in Berlin. It refers to a Rat King found in January, 1907, in the village of Capelle, near Hamm in Westphalia. The local pastor, Wigger by name, informed the zoologist Reeker, who tried to acquire it for the Provincial Museum of Westphalia. But before Reeker could move, the Zoological Institute of the University of Göttingen had secured it for its own collection.

It consisted of ten specimens of the black rat. The director of the Zoological Institute, Privy Councillor Ehlers, wrote to Dr. Heck in reply to a question that he could not explain how such a thing could have happened and that the rat's tails do not show any visible pathological changes. And he added that the Institute's taxidermist considered it impossible that this Rat King might have been made by some pranksters.

Well, this is the story.

All the cases have two things in common. It is always the black *Mus rattus* which produces a Rat King, and they have all been found during the coldest time of the year, in weather which would make the animals huddle together for warmth.

A CENTURY OF FOSSIL MAN

"THIS," I SAID TO A VISITOR, handing him a fossilized trilobite from the Silurian Period, "is due to three accidents."

"Accidents?" he repeated, wondering whether I meant what I said.

"Accidents! Three of them. The first accident was that this trilobite died under circumstances which made it possible for it to become a fossil. The second accident was that the fossil was found. And the third was that it was found by somebody who recognized it for what it was."

The whole discussion had started with the chance remark that we don't know yet whether the human race originated in Asia or in Africa. The fossil finds, I had said, are inconclusive so far, mainly because there are so few of them. Of course, it would have been appropriate if I could have handed my visitor a fossil human skull to illustrate my point. I couldn't do that because there are so few of them, and for that reason they are where they belong, in museums and in university collections. Only about a century ago no museum anywhere had a human fossil. As a matter of fact no director of a museum would have expected to see one.

And that brings me to my story.

Paleontology, the science of fossils and extinct life forms, is one of the sciences that were found essentially by one

man. He was Georges Léopold, Baron Cuvier, a French naturalist, born at Montbéliard in 1769; and the work which became the foundation of the new science was his *Recherches sur les ossemens fossiles,* or in English, *Researches on Fossil Bones.* It appeared in 1824, only eight years before Cuvier's death. Cuvier had done wonders with the scant material he had at his disposal and it was only natural that he noticed that among his fossils there, fishes and amphibians, reptiles and mammals, crustaceans and worms, but that fossils of humans were conspicuous by their absence. Man, Cuvier reasoned, must have been a late arrival on earth. The Bible, he pointed out, also said that Man had been created last. Hence Man had not been present when the other creatures became fossils and for that reason it was actually useless to look for human fossils. As Cuvier put it: *l'homme fossil n'existe pas—* "fossil man does not exist."

Just one year after Cuvier's death a Belgian paleontologist by the name of Schmerling finished a voluminous work with the title, *Account of the fossil bones found in caves in the Province of Liège.* In it he pointed out that he had found human remains in the same layers as bones of cave bears, mammoths and so forth, so that it seemed logical to assume that they had lived during the same period.

If anybody who read Schmerling's work remembered that the Baron von Schlotheim had reported the same situation from a place near Gera in Central Germany some time earlier (in 1820), he probably had the same explanation for both cases. Early settlers had buried their dead in the débris covering cave floors—and the human bones had thereby in death acquired companions they had never known when alive.

For more than three decades nothing happened to disturb these assumptions. If people did not insist on building stone houses there might have been another three or four decades

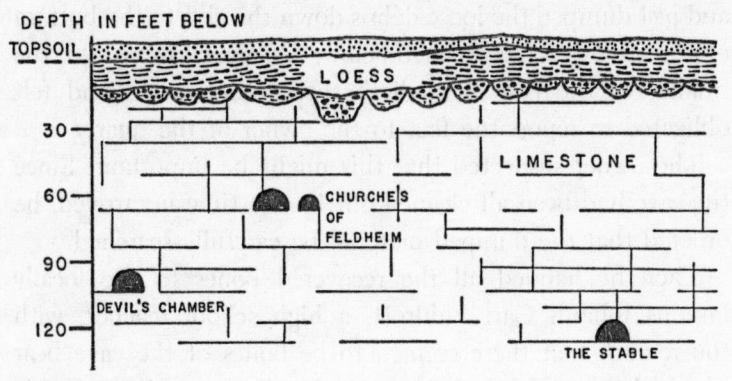

FIG. 9. The cliff of the Neanderthal Valley before it became a limestone quarry.

of peace and quiet. But people build, and one of the things they need for building is limestone.

There was one source of limestone which was not only big but easily accessible. Near the small city of Mettmann in western Germany a river, the Düssel, had cut itself a deep and narrow canyon into soft limestone. The gorge even had a name. Three centuries earlier a man by the name of Joachim Neumann had fallen in love with the romantic beauty of the gorge and had visited it again and again. Since he became famous as the author of Christian hymns which he wrote under the name of Joachim Neander, the canyon was named in his honor after his death. It was named Neander Valley, or in German, Neanderthal.

It was in 1856 that the limestone cliffs that formed the walls of the canyon became a quarry. Local people knew that there were several natural caves in the face of the cliff. They had even been given separate names. Two neighboring caves were called, nobody knows why, the Churches of Feldheim.

The workmen began their task by cleaning out the caves,

and just dumped the loose débris down the cliff to the bottom of the valley, some 70 feet below. While cleaning out the smaller of the two "churches" they found bones and felt obligated to report the fact to the owner of the quarry.

The owner suspected that this might be important. Since the cave had been all cleaned out by the time he arrived, he ordered that the dumped material be carefully searched.

Then he handed all the recovered bones to the locally famous Johann Carl Fuhlrott, a high school teacher, with the remark that these seemed to be bones of the cave bear of which he had heard so much. Fuhlrott saw immediately that the remains were human, consisting of the two upper arm bones, fragments of other arm bones, both femurs, a fragment of the pelvis and the top of the skull—the latter was one of the bones that had been dumped. Fuhlrott looked at the heavy bony ridges over the eye sockets. He noted that the whole skull was shallow with a receding forehead. He considered the femurs to be unusually heavy—and concluded that he looked at the remains of a more primitive type of man.

In a lecture he delivered soon afterwards (it was printed with some delay in 1859), he said so. But while Fuhlrott could consider himself a naturalist he knew that his knowledge of anatomy was restricted. But he also knew that Professor Schaaffhausen of the University of Bonn, an expert in human anatomy, was interested in new discoveries.

He sent the bones to Schaaffhausen, who examined and measured them with utmost care and published a report in 1858, stating that he agreed with Fuhlrott; this was an individual with strangely primitive characteristics. Being a careful man, Schaaffhausen did not attempt to determine its age, saying that he hoped that further discoveries would provide definite clues.

For a while Fuhlrott and Schaaffhausen stood alone. A Dr. PrunerBey in Paris said that these were probably just the remains of an old Celt who had died during a tribal migration. Professor Andreas Wagner in Göttingen considered it more likely that they were the bones of a Dutch sailor, while others guessed that it might be a Cossack who had taken part in the final campaign against Napoleon.

Enter now Dr. Rudolf Virchow, professor of pathology, having been appointed director of the Pathological Institute in Berlin during the same year workers began cleaning out the caves of the Neanderthal.

Since what I have to report about Virchow will sound as if he had not been too bright, I must say first that he was justly famous as a medical researcher. He reformed the sanitation system of Berlin, and he (somewhat unusually) was also very active politically. For years he was the leader of the Progressive Party of Prussia and was even elected a member of the Reichstag on the Liberal Party slate. But he had limitations. He had carefully investigated the tubercles in human lungs and written an excellent description in a highly literary style. But when it was suggested to him that these tubercles might be caused by a microorganism he had nothing but sarcasm for the little country doctor who advanced this nonsensical idea. (The little country doctor later became a famous bacteriologist. His name was Robert Koch, and in Sweden they awarded him a Nobel Prize for medicine.)

To Virchow the remains from the Neanderthal were just one more case of what he had been observing for years. He did not guess at nationality or tribe. All he could say that this man had been sick all his life. One could see the marks of his former suffering clearly.

To begin with, this individual happened to be born with an

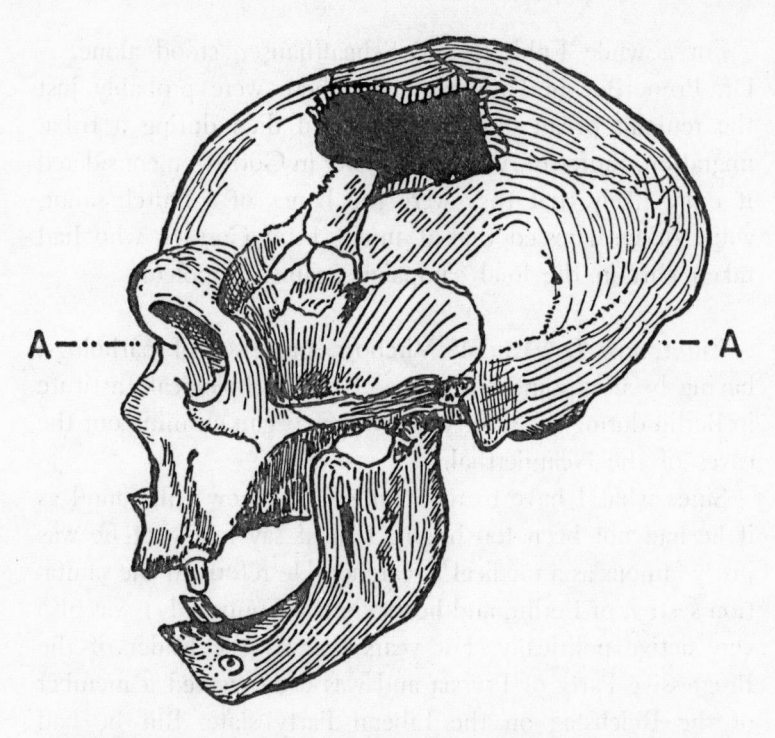

FIG. 10. Skull of a Neanderthal man (old male) from La Chapelle-aux-Saints, France. In the original skull from the Neander Valley only the portions above the Line A–A were preserved.

unusually long skull and greatly reduced sinus cavities. In his early childhood he had suffered severely from rachitis. But somehow he got over it and grew to manhood, probably to be a warrior since some minor thickenings might be due to battle injuries. However, the main features of the skull which had misled Fuhlrott (only a high school teacher, after all) and Schaaffhausen (a fine anatomist but not a pathologist) had been produced by *arthritis deformans* and old age. The outer layers of the skull had been reduced as a result of old age and new layers had formed on the inside with ossification

of the skin enclosing the brain. What was left of the arms showed signs of severe arthritis.

So said Virchow and all this was not advanced as a possibility, or even a probability. It was preceded by the sentence: "We can conclude with absolute certainty—"

One of the men who supported Fuhlrott and Schaaffhausen was Professor William King in England, also an anatomist. After stating the reasons for his position, he then proceeded to give the bones the still famous name *Homo neanderthalensis*.

FIG. 11. *Pithecanthropus erectus*, Skull No. 1 from Trinil.

But most scientists were reluctant to go along. After all, Virchow was Virchow! How could they, who were not even medical men, dispute the findings of a pathologist? There was only one such find and it was certainly possible, if unusual, that the one specimen had belonged to a sickly individual.

In the meantime—in 1864—at least definite proof that Man and extinct mammals had been contemporaneous had been found.

Jacques Boucher de Crèvecoeur de Perthes had for some years asserted that the stone artifacts he had found had been

weapons used by primitive man to hunt mammoths. But while these shaped stones, which might easily have been spearpoints, did exist, who could say what had been hunted with them?—if they had been hunting weapons at all. (And one could always point out that Boucher de Perthes had written tragedies for the stage, novels for amusement and diplomatic notes for deception. In short, that he had engaged in unscientific activities.) But the new proof, found by Edouard Lartet in a cave of the Vézère Valley in southern France, was a piece of mammoth tusk, with the outline of a mammoth scratched into it.

The final proof came from Belgium, from a cave at Spy in the vicinity of Namur. It consisted of two (incomplete) skeletons of this type of man, along with bones of extinct animals and stone implements. The particular kind of stone implements had been found earlier in France in a place named Le Moustier and had been provisionally labelled the Moustérian Culture. We now know that it is typical for the Neanderthalers. But we also know that Lartet's mammoth drawings belongs to a later time, the Magdalénien, which was not "Neanderthal."

Other finds followed. Then some scientists began to feel that the name given by Professor King was too specific. One of the suggestions made was *Homo primigenius* (or *Homo primogenitus*) but by then everybody was careful. Since the name means "first" man it was not accepted—maybe somebody would find a still older form. But many scientists were willing to go along with the suggestion *Homo diluvianus*. The geological period preceding the present period was then generally called *Diluvium*, so that the name was suggestive of the time. (Now the geological present is called the "holocene" and the preceding period, for which "Ice Age" is another synonym, goes under the name of "pleistocene.")

As for the still older form it already had a name. Professor
Ernst Haeckel, reasoning that at one time a form halfway
between ape and man must have existed, had coined the
term *Pithecanthropus* or "apeman" for this hypothetical being. (In his work *General Morphology*, first published in
1886.) And a Dutch physician, Eugène Dubois by name, had
joined the Dutch Colonial Services for the purpose of being
sent to the tropics, where he was going to look for the common ancestor of both present-day man *and* of Neanderthal
man.

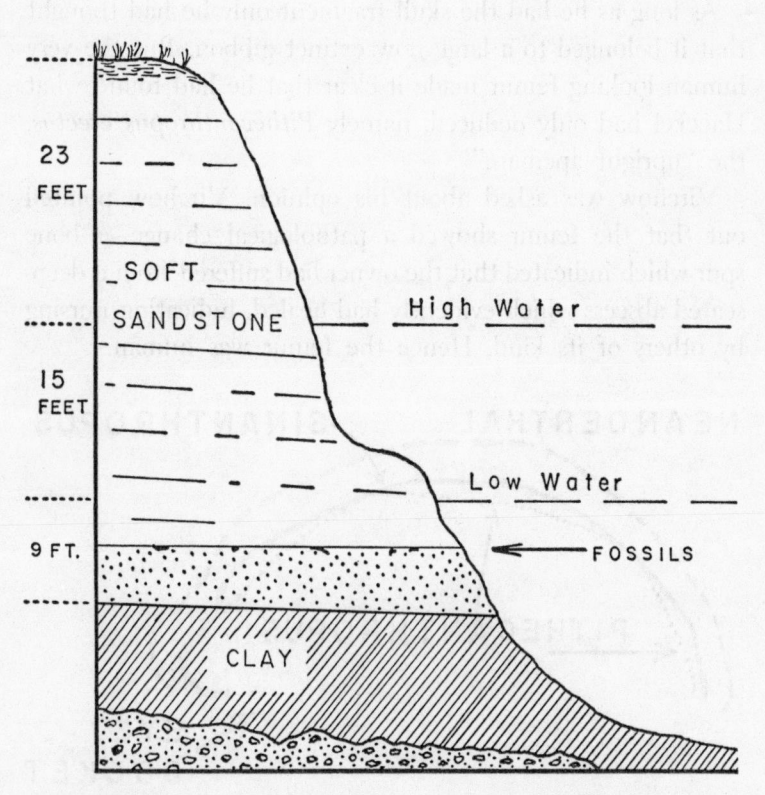

Fig. 12. Profile of the Bengawan river where Pithecanthropus
was found.

He was sent to Java. There he learned that fossils had been discovered in the banks of the Bengawan river near a place called Trinil. When the river was at its lowest point in 1890 he began to dig.

His first success, as far as human remains were concerned, was a single tooth, but Dubois said to himself that that tooth could have belonged to a now extinct species of ape. However, in 1894 he could shout success. He had found the roof of a skull first and later and some distance—about 30 feet— away a left femur.

As long as he had the skull fragment only he had thought that it belonged to a large now extinct gibbon. But the very human looking femur made it clear that he had found what Haeckel had only deduced, namely *Pithecanthropus erectus*, the "upright apeman."

Virchow was asked about his opinion. Virchow pointed out that the femur showed a pathological change—a bone spur which indicated that the owner had suffered from a deep-seated abscess which evidently had healed, indicating nursing by others of its kind. Hence the femur was human.

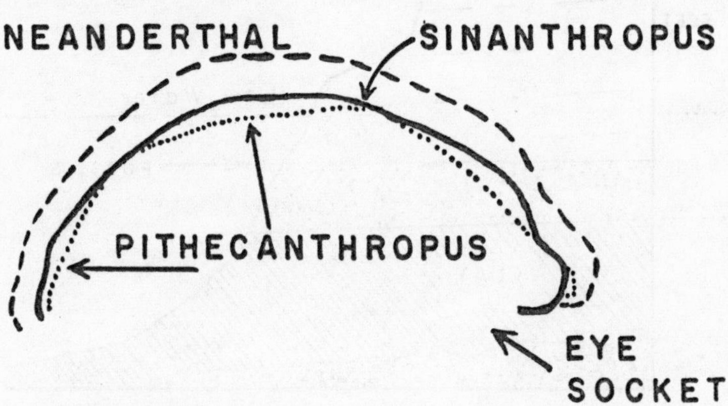

FIG. 13. Profiles of the tops of the skulls of three early forms of humans.

The skull, on the other hand, belonged to a large extinct gibbon. The two bones had nothing to do with each other; after all they had been found some distance apart. Later on Virchow changed his opinion. The layer was probably too old to contain human remains, and if there had been a gibbon-like creature of this size it might have walked upright because it was too heavy to live in the treetops like the gibbons of our time. By that time Virchow was in his seventies and respect had somewhat waned. Others went ahead with their investigation. They were determined to find out whether this was, or had been, an apeman or not. They did not deny that an apeman *might* have existed.

"Brain capacity" became the new battle cry.

Living humans—pygmies excluded, but otherwise without regard as to skin color, nationality, religion or credit rating—have an average brain capacity of about 1500 cubic centimeters. The Neanderthal types from Germany, Belgium, France and elsewhere in Europe averaged 1200 cubic centimeters or a little more. A large gorilla, largest of the apes, fell a little short of 700 cubic centimeters.

How about Pithecanthropus? Since the skull roof was incomplete there was a little leeway in computing the former content, but the disagreement was minor. It ranged from 900 to 935 cc. Nicely in the middle, between gorilla on the one side and *Homo neanderthalensis* on the other.

The unsolved problem that remained was one of distance. The valley of the Bengawan was very far from the valley of the Vézère or even from Croatia where more Neanderthal men had been found. However, if you discounted the arms of the Sunda Sea between Java and the Asian mainland (and who could say whether they had existed then?), there were no insurmountable obstacles between Java and France. Even

a slowly wandering tribe, if it kept going, could do it in just
one generation.

The sequence seemed clear: some unknown ancestor first,
then Pithecanthropus, then Neanderthal man, then modern
man.

If you believed in this sequence in Europe in 1900 you were
under faint suspicion of being a socialist, unless you had a
Ph.D. to indicate that you knew what you were talking
about. By 1914 you could believe in this sequence without
arousing political suspicions, though a doctorate was still helpful.

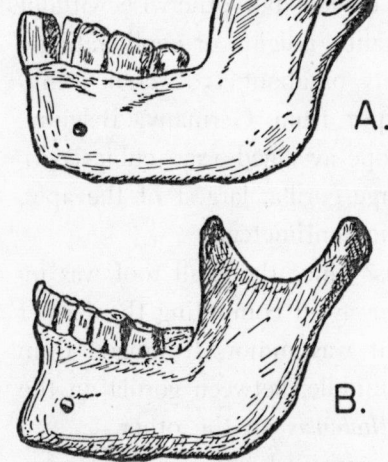

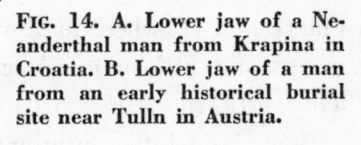

FIG. 14. A. Lower jaw of a Neanderthal man from Krapina in
Croatia. B. Lower jaw of a man
from an early historical burial
site near Tulln in Austria.

Now we know much more, but aren't so sure any more.

On the one hand we have more reason to think that Pithecanthropus was ancestral to Neanderthal man. On the other
hand there is a great deal of doubt whether Neanderthal
man is ancestral to us.

Let me take the latter problem first, if only because I sometimes encountered a surprised reaction when I say so.

How could Neanderthal man *not* be ancestral, since he was around a long time earlier? I think that a comparison with dog-breeding will illustrate the point. The animal which was to become the domesticated dog was probably a small jackal-like form. Slowly it was bred larger into forms somewhat resembling today's greyhound, though smaller. Then (this is just an example, not dog-breeding history) let us say that breeders produced the English bulldog, a dog of specialized shape. Much later other breeders went after another shape of dog, say a poodle.

But they would start with the original stock, not with the specialized bulldog.

Neanderthal man would correspond to the bulldog of this example, an early and specialized offshoot. Some skulls have been found that look like Neanderthal man, but with less pronounced special features. Some researchers have assumed that they are hybrid forms. But it is just as possible that they are an older and not yet so specialized form of Neanderthalers.

The history of the discoveries of human fossils since Dubois unearthed Pithecanthropus would make a very long chapter by itself, but at this point we need only the most pronounced highlights. In 1929 Dr. Davidson Black discovered skulls near Peking which were subsequently labelled *Sinanthropus pekinensis*, with a brain capacity higher than that of Pithecanthropus but still less than Neanderthal. More specimens of Pithecanthropus were added from Sangiran (Java) by Dr. G. H. R. von Koenigswald. A very large Neanderthal man turned up in Rhodesia, Africa. And southern Africa added a whole series of small forerunners of Man which are collectively called the australopithecines. (The word has nothing to do with the Australian continent, it merely means "southern monkeys.")

One theory has it that our own ancestors originated in Africa and migrated northward to Europe to turn into early Europeans. Those who stayed in Africa were the ancestors of the Africans of today. According to that theory, the Neanderthal type originated in eastern Asia and performed a westward migration to Europe rather late in their history. But no decision on whether this theory or rival theories are correct can be made at the moment.

Since the question of who is ancestral to whom cannot yet be decided, researchers have sorted all human fossils into three groups, once more using brain volume as the criterion. They distinguish:

(A) the australopithecines, with a brain capacity of 450 to 700 cc;

(B) *Homo erectus*, with a brain capacity of 775 to 1200 cc;

(C) *Homo sapiens*, with a brain capacity of over 1200 cc.

This sorting scheme puts Pithecanthropus into the *Homo erectus* group, but puts the late European Neanderthalers (as well as the Neanderthaler from Rhodesia) into the *Homo sapiens* group. To repeat, this is essentially a method of sorting, and does not necessarily indicate actual relationships. To clear that question up we need many more of the "triple accidents."

CHAPTER V

SLOW LIGHTNING

JUST AS DICTIONARIES AND ENCYCLOPEDIAS are in need of constant revision, our popular sayings should be amended too from time to time. The man who says "Everything that goes up must come down" should be obliged to add "unless it reaches escape velocity." Likewise the man who says "with the speed of lightning" should make the provision "but I don't mean ball lightning."

Ball lightning may move as slowly as three inches per second. It may even stand still for a short time. Ball lightning is one of the things I have yet to see myself. I also have never seen a volcanic eruption, but this problem (if it preyed on my mind) could be easily solved by flying to the scene of an erupting volcano. Ball lightning is, as far as we know, pure chance. But I do know that my chance would be somewhat better in Europe north of the Alps.

So many Americans have never even heard of ball lightning because it happens to be very rare in North America. That a natural phenomenon should be rare in one area and not rare in another seems somewhat incredible at first glance. But it is a fact, for example, that "twisters" are rare in northern Europe (and if they do occur they are quite weak compared to their American counterpart) and ball lightning, while by no means a frequent phenomenon in Europe, seems to be positively abundant compared to its rarity in the United States.

Instead of describing ball lightning and how it behaves, let me give a condensed quotation of a case which took place in Paris just after noon on July 5, 1852, and for which sworn statements were filed with the French Academy of Science.

It was during the summer and for this reason the fireplace in the apartment was not in use. According to custom the front opening of the fireplace had been closed by a wooden frame to which stout wrapping paper had been pasted. Likewise the curved stovepipe on top of the fireplace had been taken down and the round hole in the wall into which the stovepipe fitted had also been pasted over with wrapping paper.

The apartment in the Rue St. Jacques, next to the Val-de-Grâce Church, was located on the fourth floor and occupied by a tailor. He had finished lunch but remained seated at the table because there was a thunderstorm going on. Some time (not immediately) after a very strong thunderclap, the frame closing the fireplace was pushed out as if by a strong gust of wind. Then a fiery ball, the size of a human head, emerged from the opening and meandered slowly about the room, a few inches above the floor. The ball was brightly luminous but did not radiate any heat.

It approached the tailor's feet ("like a cat," he said later) but the man did not wish to be touched. He pulled his feet back without rising from the chair and watched the ball which slowly moved around in the center of the room. Then it suddenly rose to about one yard above the floor. It became slightly elongated and flew to the hole in the wall. The paper was peeled off without being damaged in the process and the ball disappeared in the chimney. After it had climbed to the top of the chimney—very slowly—it exploded with a loud noise, destroying the top portion of the chimney.

To somebody who reads such a description for the first

time, all this sounds pretty far-fetched. But to anyone who is conversant with the behavior of ball lightning this is merely typical, as can easily be seen from another case, this time from Königsberg, East Prussia.

The owner of a beer garden outside the city, a Herr Babinski, rendered the following description: "We had a strong thunderstorm during the early afternoon hours and my beer garden was hit by lightning which, however, did not cause any damage. Immediately afterward there appeared, at about my eye level, a reddish rotating ball approximately 16 inches in diameter, in the open door of the restaurant kitchen. Since the other door of the kitchen was open too there was a considerable draft. The sphere, rotating all the time, passed quite a number of people, climbed up along the wiring of the electric bell, was then apparently caught by the draft, then moved along another electric wire to the stable and exploded with a loud noise above the door of the stable."

That ball lightning likes to travel along a conductor is almost proverbial. One was seen on May 19, 1925, in the Dutch city of The Hague. It moved for a very considerable distance along a streetcar rail, then jumped into a transformer box and disappeared.

A real estate owner in East Prussia, Reich by name, had the interesting experience of being pursued by ball lightning. In the evening of "the Day of Pentecost, 1890, at 8 P.M." Herr Reich drove his carriage along a country road lined on both sides by wire fences. His carriage was of the open type, with four rather large iron-rimmed wooden wheels, running on iron axles and normally drawn by two, but since this was in horse-breeding East Prussia, more likely by four horses.

"The sky was covered with clouds, but it was not raining. Two very bright head-sized balls appeared on both wire fences, moving along the fences at the same rate as the carriage.

Many sparks jumped from these balls to the carriage axles. The horses shied and increased their pace but the faster the carriage moved the faster the fire balls moved until we came to the end of the wire fences. There both balls, collapsed into nothing, without an explosion but with a noise like crumbling a sheet of paper."

Finally a case which happened near the small town of Bischofswerda in Saxony on April 29, 1925, at half an hour after noon. It was one of the rare cases of a violent lightning ball which was described by many witnesses.

Taking it chronologically, the first witness was a mailman by the name of Fasold who asserted that he had not known about ball lightning. He was on the road and saw "a grayish-black cloud from which something dangled which almost looked like a trouser leg. Suddenly something fell from this dangling trouser leg which looked like a golden beer barrel. This body landed near a telephone pole with a loud crash and I had the impression that it came apart, somewhat like emptying a basket of potatoes. From this heap real lightning jumped and one of the strokes hit the school. I was so surprised that I can't say whether the crash was followed by real thunder or not, but I know that it was raining a bit before and that a little hail fell afterward." Mailman Fasold also stated that the trees looked for a short time like Christmas trees, as if they had candles at the tips of the twigs.

At the school they saw a lightning ball move along the telephone wire (later it turned out that it had first smashed a transformer box) traveling at about the rate of a briskly walking man. The ball moved into the apartment of the teacher (which was part of the school building). The teacher (male) was using the telephone and stated that the lightning ball threw him to the floor. The telephone itself was not damaged. The door to the teacher's apartment had a glass pane; later it

was found to have two holes both perfectly circular and clean. One of these two holes was the size of a silver dollar, the other that of a quarter (the German report mentions other coins, of course, but of the size of the American coins named) and it is thought that the bigger hole was that caused by the entry while the smaller one was caused on leaving, when the ball had expended some of its energy. Like other lightning balls, it moved along wires, but this one melted the wires into tiny spherules of metal. But it did not ignite inflammable material in its direct path—also a common feature of all the reports, lightning balls have been known to melt down quarter-inch bronze rods, but nestle in excelsior without igniting it—and then proceeded along a ceiling. It must have moved under the plaster, because the plaster was forced off. Then it broke through a wall and disappeared.

Afterward additional damage was found, presumably caused before the lightning ball entered the school building. The telephone wire had been melted down for 700 feet of its length, several telephone poles, including a fifteen-foot support of angle iron, were splintered, a cable 2½ feet below ground was severed as if with a stroke with a sharp axe, the trunk of a cherry tree was split and several men working near the road were thrown to the ground without harming them otherwise. And all this, as far as the witnesses could recall, without making any noise at all!

While the phenomenon seems to be somewhat more frequent in northern Europe than in North America, there exist a fair number of reports from the North American continent, too. One case, of which I have only a verbal description, was told to me by an American Air Force officer in Denver in 1955. Somewhere in the outskirts of the city a highway has been cut through a hill, but a high tension wire spans the gap. The officer—he was not driving—observed a bright bluish

ball traveling along the high tension wire, "about as fast as a man walking briskly." The officer, who had seen the occurrence but did not know about the existence of ball lightning until he talked to me, had nothing to add. He remembered that it was during the evening at about 10 P.M. local time and that it was a warm night, but if there was a thunderstorm nearby he did not know about it. He could not see what happened to the ball, he just saw it move along the wire.

Another case—the date must have been 1925 or 1926—was reported to me by letter by a gentleman who now lived in Westfield, New Jersey:

"Thirty-five years ago I was a camper in a boys camp in Chicopee, Pennsylvania. It was mid or late afternoon. I was sitting on my bunk next to an open window, looking outside at the general area of the camp quadrangle which had just been inundated by a severe thunderstorm. Because of the storm we were in our cabins rather than at an activity. All the windows of these cabins were usually kept open. Suddenly, I saw coming directly toward me a ball of fire, yellow golden in color, about the size of a basketball. It was moving fairly quickly . . . in retrospect I would guess that it was travelling 25 or 30 miles per hour. As I saw it heading toward my window I pulled my head back away from the opening in time to see it pass by my head, go through the cabin to the other side and out an opposite window . . . There was no damage to anyone in the cabin or to the cabin itself. The ball did not follow a conductor, at least I do not recall any wiring going in the same direction. Perhaps the electrical inlet for the cabin was outside my window. I do not know. There was no noise whatsoever. This I do remember."

A very recent case was reported in a letter to the editor of *Science* (published in the issue dated February 11, 1966) by

Frederick B. Mohr of the Aerospace Technology Division of the Library of Congress.

"On August 25, 1965, . . . my uncle and aunt, Mr. and Mrs. Robert B. Greenlee, were relaxing on their fiberglass-screened, roofed patio in Dunnellon, Florida. The temperature was in the 90's, the sky was overcast, and there was a slight drizzle; the Greenlees had heard thunder some distance to the west of their immediate vicinity. Mrs. Greenlee and a neighbor, Mrs. Riggs, were seated a few feet apart in aluminum chairs, and Mr. Greenlee was standing about three feet from Mrs. Greenlee. Mrs. Greenlee had just swatted a fly when a ball of lightning the size of a basketball appeared immediately in front of her. The ball was later described as being of a color and brightness comparable to the flash seen in arc welding, with a fuzzy appearance around the edges. Mrs. Riggs did not see the ball itself, but saw the flyswatter "edged in fire" dropping on the floor. The movement of the ball to the floor was accompanied by a report "like a shotgun blast." The entire incident was over in seconds.

None of the witnesses felt any heat from the ball, and Mrs. Greenlee showed no signs of external injuries, although she complained of pain in the back of her neck and has had occasional headaches since. The explosion was heard by a neighbor about 150 feet away, and it was subsequently learned that another neighbor's electric range had been shorted out at the same time. There was no damage of any sort at the Greenlees, nor were there any marks on the patio floor where the flyswatter had fallen."

The overall picture that can be extracted from these reports is that a rather large amount of electrical energy is concentrated in a small volume; that this concentration is stable only for a short while; that the lightning ball pre-

fers to follow electrical conductors which it may or may not melt in the process; that it does not set fires and does not electrocute people. Several people have been touched by lightning balls, much against their will and inclination, in most cases without experiencing any sensation. Some people were thrown to the ground, but without other harm than that caused by the fall itself. Most of the time the end of the ball is by way of an explosion which is described as sounding like the sharp crack of an enormous whip. But the damage caused by the explosion is minor. Often the balls just go out. In most cases the witnesses cannot tell where the ball came from. In a few cases it has been seen to fall from a cloud, but very slowly, as if its weight were negligible. In a few other cases witnesses think that it followed the path of a normal lightning stroke which preceded it.

Sometimes lightning balls have appeared without an accompanying thunderstorm. Most of them, however, were associated with thunderstorms, though it is almost a rule that they appear at the end of the storm—the end for the area in question, that is.

Now, how do they originate?

The answer is that we do not know.

During the 1920s a Norwegian engineer by the name of A. Nielson once obtained what he thought to be an artificial lightning ball by the accidental short-circuiting of a 12,000-volt generator. This ball rose up in the air and then disappeared (dissipated?), showing an atypical behavior. It probably was not a lightning ball at all, but just a cloud of superheated air and metal vapor that happened to assume a spherical shape.

German electrical engineers in Berlin, at about the same time, wondered whether a lightning ball might be the result of two "normal" strokes of lightning crossing paths. They

made experiments in a high voltage laboratory with this idea in mind, but were unsuccessful. Either they could not get their artificial lightning strokes to cross paths, or else that is not the way ball lightning is caused. At a later date, in 1954, the well-known Russian atomic scientist P. L. Kapitsa undertook a theoretical study of ball lightning. His reasoning is very interesting, though I feel certain that it is not the answer. Academician Kapitsa pointed out that the cloud resulting from an atomic explosion lasts a very short time in spite of its enormous size. Such an explosion cloud consists of gases which Kapitsa assumes to be 100 per cent ionized. Ball lightning, which must consist at least partly of ionized gases, is known to last for a minute and longer, and its size, compared to that of an atomic explosion cloud, is virtually microscopic. Hence, Kapitsa reasoned, the lightning ball must have a steady "energy income" during its lifetime. When this "energy income" is cut off, the ball shrivels into nothing; it just goes out. If the supply is cut off very suddenly the ball collapses, its collapse causing a shock wave which makes the sharp crack. The noise, then, would be that of an implosion rather than that of an explosion. (The nature of the sound is no clue as to which it is, unfortunately. Either an explosion or an implosion can cause such a sharp crack.)

Kapitsa's guess as to what feeds the lightning ball for the duration of its existence is natural radio waves, presumably generated by the storm cloud and reflected by the ground. A very interesting idea, but this is really explaining one unknown by another one. It seems logical that a thundercloud might generate radio waves, but we don't know to what extent. Kapitsa is too much of a scientist to insist that his idea is right just because it is his idea. His paper begins with the sentence: "The nature of ball lightning is not as yet understood."

But while I don't think that Kapitsa's reasoning, novel as
it is, has solved the problem of the origin of ball lightning,
he quoted a case reported in *Nature* (No. 563, April 1952)
where a lightning ball entered the interior of an airplane flying
at an altitude of 9200 feet. This is the first recorded instance
of high-altitude ball lightning that has come to my attention.
But I have always suspected that high-altitude ball lightning
exists. When, near the end of the Second World War, we
got those reports about the so-called "foo fighters"—balls of
light following our airplanes near their wingtips for long
distance without ever doing anything—I immediately thought
of the two lightning balls which had accompanied the open
carriage on the country road.

Naturally I have not quoted all the cases on record—they
would fill a book. In fact, they *do* fill a book; it was written
by Dr. Walther Brand in 1923 and published during the same
year in Hamburg by the publisher Henri Grand. (Its title
is *Der Kugelblitz*.)

But one more case should be mentioned. Early in 1961
I received a letter from a Canadian fighter pilot who told
me that he and a friend of his (presumably a fellow pilot)
were flying a fast fighter jet over British Columbia at an altitude of 48,000 feet. They were flying so high to avoid the
tops of spectacular cumulonimbus towers which were building
up over the area. Because the cloud formations were so spectacular the friend of my correspondent took pictures. In a
black thundercloud they saw (and photographed) a luminous object. "The second shot shows it obscured by a tongue
of cloud but shining through it. The ball must have been
about the size of an aircraft [remember that fighter planes are
under discussion, not passenger liners] if the visual clues are
consistent. Although it appeared to the eye to have well-de-
fined edges, according to the witnesses, the photo shows it

definitely fuzzy. Maybe they radiate to the ultraviolet or higher as well."

Apparently in the thundercloud building up a lightning ball did form. That there happened to be somebody around to see and to photograph it is a lucky coincidence but not new in itself. Lightning balls have been seen to fall out of clouds; hence they must have been in the clouds before. What is new is the estimate of size, which is about a dozen or more times larger than any lightning ball observed near the ground.

Are they larger when forming and contract as they age?

Or does the size correspond more or less to the ambient air pressure? Since the planes were at 48,000 feet to clear the tops of the towers this lightning ball may well have been at 42,000 feet or thereabouts, where the air pressure is down to about 130 millimeters of mercury.

Too bad that with such a fascinating subject we have to depend on luck only!

CHAPTER VI

THE MOON WORM

"WHEN THIS SHRUB IS COVERED with blossoms," the Samoans told the English traveler Powell, "it is time to see whether the boats and the baskets are ready." Powell knew that the blossoms of the shrub in question would be bright scarlet and he had provided himself with the information that its scientific name is *Erythrina indica.* "Then," the Samoans continued, "when the *Sisi* plant [related to the myrtle] blooms, we look for the Moon. Soon after, the Moon will be just above the horizon toward evening (west) at dawn. Ten days later we will have *Mblalolo lailai* and a month after that *Mblalolo levu.* You'll see."

Powell noted that the islander's face was beaming in anticipation when saying *Mblalolo lailai.* It was a big event for the Samoans as well as for the Fiji Islanders, these two feasts coming a month apart. The term "feast" is to be taken in its primitive meaning, an occasion where everybody present eats until nothing can possibly be stuffed inside any more.

It must be remembered here that these islands are in the southern hemisphere; though the two months in question are October and November, this was a spring festival.

The words *levu* and *lailai,* as I was informed by Professor Charles F. Hocket of the University of Hawaii, are Fijian. *Levu* means big or major, while *lailai* means small or minor.

As for the word *Mblalolo* somebody, possibly Powell, adapted it to western tongues by changing it to "palolo."

And now we are ready for the story.

During the night of the *Mblalolo* the Samoans did not go to sleep. Late, after midnight, they rowed out to sea, but not very far. While the men handled the oars the women had loosely woven baskets ready. Other women and boys who did not yet have adult status sat at the shore with their baskets. All of a sudden, at 4 A.M., the sea became alive. Worm-like shapes wiggled at the surface, as suddenly as if they had been ejected by a submerged explosion. Within less than ten minutes the surface was solidly covered with worm bodies, wiggling, squirming, in steady motion.

The girls scooped them into the boats with their baskets and everybody aboard—and ashore—started to eat. The worms were so thick that one did not even need a basket; just reaching into the water with bare hands would bring edible results.

But only for an hour or so.

At the end of that time the ocean would look cloudy, as if milk had been poured into it, but no more worms. The boats returned to shore with their catch; the gourmets preferred their worms baked in palm leaves. And countless runners were waiting ashore too, to carry baskets to those living farther inland. On Samoa, as reported by a later investigator, the islanders had organized relays of runners to get the delicacy inland just as fast as well-exercised legs could do it.

These were the cultural aspects, the two feast days, or rather nights in spring, based on the sudden appearance of an edible marine creature.

The zoological aspects were not quite as simple.

That the things which came to the surface in uncountable multitudes were worms was beyond any doubt. In fact they

were annelid worms, of the same general type as our earth-
worm, but a large marine version. They came in two colors.
One was darkish green or bluish green; these were filled with
eggs, literally to the bursting point, for that's the way they
disappeared an hour or so later, by bursting. The other kind
was whitish or yellowish or about the color of egg yolk. These
contained the male sperm.

As for the length of the worms, the reports were at first
a bit confusing; any length between one inch and fourteen
inches was reported. But it was soon realized that the shorter
ones were literally pieces, segments broken off the bigger
ones.

So far things were nice and clear; the two *Mblalolo* nights
were the mating periods of these worms. As the Samoans
had said all along, the two mating nights were one month
apart, but they did not fall on the same dates in successive
years. Outside of these two mating nights, nobody had ever
seen a *Mblalolo*. It obviously lived at the bottom of the sea
normally.

The worm was first given the scientific name *Palolo viridis*,
the second word with reference to the green color of the
egg-containing segments. A little later the scientific name
was changed to *Eunice viridis*. It was quite clear from the
outset that the sexes were very strictly separated, each worm
being either male or female. But the early observers reported
with headshaking that all the worms were headless.

Samoa, at the time I am talking about (ca. 1890), was
still an independent kingdom with three countries wielding
a good deal of influence: the United States (which had
leased the harbor of Pago Pago—pronounced Pango
Pango—), Great Britain and Germany. In 1898 trouble developed which led to the withdrawal of Great Britain and a

partition of the Samoan islands between the United States and Germany.

But before this political development took place a German zoologist, Dr. Benedikt Friedländer, had arrived on the scene. His first attempt had been to find the palolo in its natural habitat and under pre-swarming conditions. He fished for it a fair distance from the shore and at considerable depth. Of course he caught some marine worms but none of them was *Palolo viridis*. While thinking about the equipment he would need to fish at even greater depths (and, logically, still farther from shore) he talked to Samoans.

Somewhat puzzled, he told after his return to Berlin that the information coming from "an old woman" had been best—presumably he expected that young and actively fishing men should know most about it. The old woman told Dr. Friedländer that the worms lived in cracks of the coral rock, not very deep and close to the shore. Benedikt Friedländer, willing to try everything once—he even tried the green palolo segments when they swarmed, reporting that they tasted like almost unsalted Russian caviar—had a number of blocks of dead coral hauled up. Yes, there was *Palolo viridis*, complete with head and up to about 40 inches long.

The old woman had also told him that the worms in the coral rock, if placed in pails of sea water, would swarm at the same time as the worms in the open. Friedländer was too busy to make the experiment but did not doubt the statement; he just stated honestly that he had not verified it.

Once you had the complete worm (Fig. 15) many of the puzzles became quite clear. The worm as a whole does not swarm. The head and about the first fifth of its length stays quietly where it always lives. The latter part of the body, the portion containing the eggs or the sperm, is detached at the right moment, rises squirming to the surface and, after

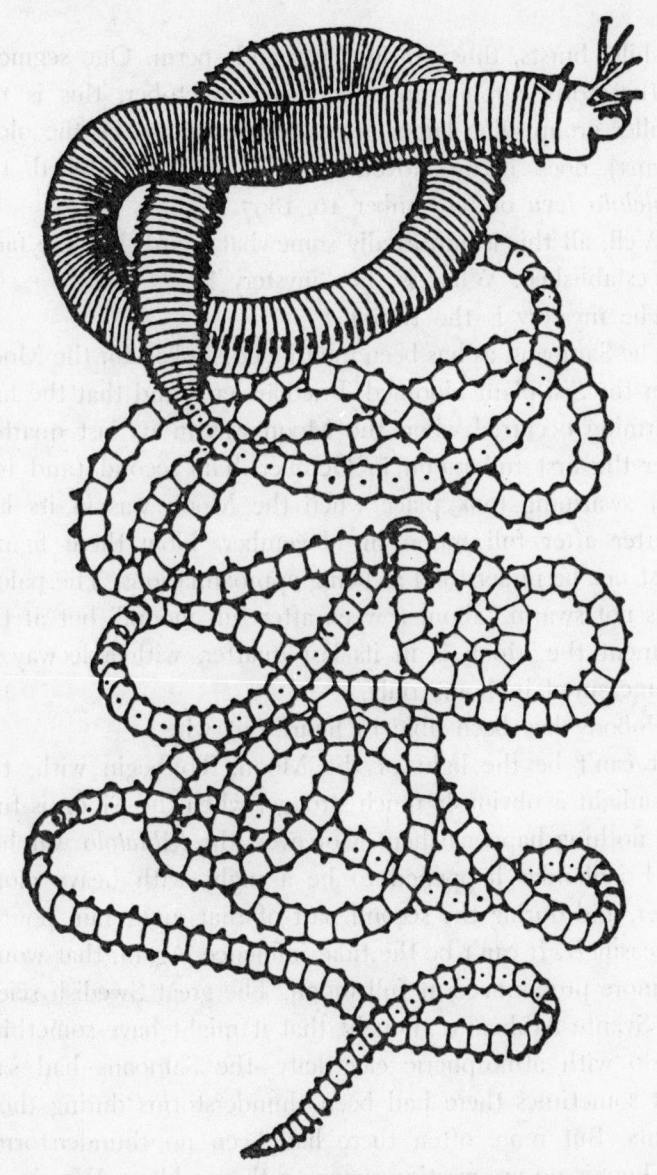

FIG. 15. *Eunice viridis,* **alias Palolo. Complete specimen; the spawning break occurs where segments become roundish.**

a while, bursts, thus uniting eggs and sperm. One segment of the worm population does this in October; this is the smaller group. The larger group (suspected to be the older worms) does it in November. Friedländer watched the *Mblalolo levu* of November 16, 1897.

Well, all this is admittedly somewhat weird, but the facts are established. What is the "mystery"?

The mystery is the timing.

The Samoans, as has been mentioned, looked for the Moon after the *Sisi* plant bloomed. Friedländer found that the first swarming occurred when the Moon was in its last quarter, after the first full moon in October. The second (and bigger) swarming took place when the Moon was in its last quarter after full moon in November. Now these figures must *not* be understood as being approximations. The palolo does not swarm "about a week after full moon," but at the moment the Moon is in its last quarter, with a leeway to be measured in hours only.

Nobody has been able to figure out why.

It can't be the light of the Moon. To begin with, the moonlight is obviously much stronger when the Moon is full, but nothing happens then. Moreover, the *Mblalolo* watched by Friedländer happened to be a night with heavy cloud cover, and during the second part of that night rain poured unceasingly. It can't be the tidal influence. Again, that would be more pronounced at full moon. The great Swedish scientist Svante Arhhenius thought that it might have something to do with atmospheric electricity—the Samoans had said that sometimes there had been thunderstorms during those nights. But more often there had been no thunderstorms.

There is no use wasting space on the problem. We simply do not know.

But since Friedländer's day we have found something

else: a related worm with the same behavior, this time in the northern hemisphere and in the Atlantic. It is *Eunice fucata* of the island Loggerhead Key in the West Indies. It also swarms when the Moon is in its last quarter, but here it is the last quarter following the full moon in July.

Because the numbers are smaller, it is not as spectacular as around Samoa and the Fiji Islands. But the performance is the same and the mystery of the timing is the same.

CHAPTER VII

THE WHEELS OF POSEIDON

THERE EXISTS a rare and awe-inspiring phenomenon in the Indian Ocean. It has been reported often enough so that there can be no doubt about its existence, though a really satisfactory explanation is still lacking. Nor does it have a generally accepted name, the title of this chapter being my suggestion for one.

Like most people I had never heard of it until the January 1952 issue of the *United States Naval Institute Proceedings* landed on my desk, containing a report by Commander J. R. Bodler, USNR. In retrospect I wonder a little bit how Commander Bodler convinced the editors of this journal that he had actually seen what he described, for the story sounded sufficiently incredible to have been the result of overindulgence in some exotic food.

Like a good seaman, Commander Bodler supplied all the detail: "Date, 14 November 1949, Time 1830 GMT, Position 26°17.5′ N., 56°51′ E. Wind NW'ly force 1. Sea calm with slight surface ripples; no swell. Air 75° F., sea 83° F. Visibility: very good. A clear bright night with no moon. Course 157° T., speed through the water 11.6 knots, actual speed over the bottom approx. 9 knots due to strong head current. At no time were any unusual deviations of the magnetic compass observed."

In landman's language this means that the vessel, bound

for India, had come from some port on the Persian Gulf and was about to enter the Gulf of Oman. At that time the third mate called the skipper to the bridge. "About four points on the port bow, toward the coast of Iran, there was a luminous band which seemed to pulsate." At first Commander Bodler thought that it was near the horizon; then it turned out that it was below the horizon, in the water. The luminous patch, which clearly pulsated, happened to be on course of the vessel so that the two drew together.

"At a distance of about a mile from the ship," to quote Commander Bodler, "it was apparent that the disturbance was roughly circular in shape, about 1000 to 1500 feet in diameter. The pulsations could now be seen to be caused by a revolving motion of the entire pattern about a rather ill-defined center; with streaks of light like the beams of searchlights, radiating outward from the center and revolving (in a counterclockwise direction) like the spokes of a gigantic wheel."

A sketch drawn by Commander Bodler shows that the outer ends of the "spokes" lagged behind, as if whatever made up the spokes of the wheels moved with a nearly uniform speed, so that the extreme ends naturally lagged.

"For several minutes the vessel occupied the approximate center of the phenomenon. Slightly curved bands of light crossed the bow, passed rapidly down the port side from bow to stern, and up the starboard side from aft, forward. The bands of luminance seemed to pass a given point at about half-second intervals. . . . The central 'hub' of the phenomenon drew gradually to starboard and passed aft; becoming more and more distant on the starboard quarter. While it was still in sight, several miles astern and appearing, by this time, as a pulsating band of light, a repetition of the same manifestation appeared fine on the starboard bow. This

was slightly smaller in area than the first, and a trifle less brilliant.

"Approximately half an hour later, a third repetition of this manifestation was observed. The general characteristics, direction of rotation, etc., were the same as the others, but this one was much smaller and less brilliant. Its diameter was not over 800 to 1000 feet and compared to the other two was unimpressive."

I could not recall having read another report just like this. Some fifty years ago somebody whose name I don't remember wrote a description of an especially impressive example of phosphorescence he had witnessed from board of a passenger liner bound from the Mediterranean for Yokohama. He wrote that sometimes it looked as if the ship were the center of a gigantic fireworks pinwheel—but such a comparison can well be made, as everybody knows who has seen it, without experiencing the phenomenon described by Commander Bodler.

Immediately after the publication of the foregoing I received a letter from Mr. Charles R. Tanner of Cincinnati, Ohio, who wrote:

"Dig up Charles Fort's *Book of the Damned* Chapter XXI. It seems remarkable to me that the two phenomena should be noted in the same part of the world. When I first read the *Book of the Damned* I remember being impressed by this letter, which seemed to have a ring of truth that not one in a thousand of Fort's phenomena do have. It stuck in my mind all these years for that reason."

Naturally I reached for Fort's book. I have the one-volume edition published by Henry Holt in 1941. In that edition the twenty-first chapter of the *Book of the Damned* begins, on p. 270, with a letter that appeared in the now defunct

magazine *Knowledge* on Dec. 28, 1883. With very minor condensations it reads as follows: "I am tempted to ask for an explanation of the following which I saw when on board the British India Company's steamer *Patna,* while on a voyage up the Persia Gulf. In May, 1880, on a dark night, about 11:30 P.M., there suddenly appeared on each side of the ship an enormous luminous wheel, whirling around, the spokes of which seemed to brush the ship along. The spokes would be 200 or 300 yards long . . . Each wheel contained about sixteen spokes, and, although the wheels must have been some 500 or 600 yards in diameter, the spokes could be distinctly seen all the way round. The phosphorescent gleam seemed to glide along flat on the surface of the sea, no light being visible in the air above the water . . . I may mention that the phenomenon was also seen by Captain Avern, of the *Patna,* and Mr. Manning, third officer."

The signature was "Lee Fore Brace," and below that was a P.S. reading: "The wheels advanced along with the ship for about 20 minutes."

It was probably the silly signature which inspired somebody signing himself "A. Mc. D." to write a letter to the editor which contained the requested explanation: "It is that before 11:30 P.M. there had been numerous accidents to the 'main brace' and that it had required splicing so often that almost any ray of light would have taken a rotary motion."

In the issue dated January 25, 1884, the original correspondent, now signing his letter "J. W. Robertson," complained: "I do think it's rather unjust to say a man is drunk because he sees something out of the common."

Charles Fort, after meandering around for several pages in his characteristic and intensely annoying manner, then does quote a few more cases of the same sort of phenomenon. One (the source is identified as *Journal of the Royal*

Meteorological Society, 28–29) states that Captain Hoseason of the ship *Kilwa* saw vast "ripples" of light appeared suddenly. "Ripple" followed upon "ripple." The light was faint, appeared suddenly and died out gradually in about fifteen minutes. Time and place: April 4, 1901, about 8:30 P.M. in the Persian Gulf.

Another one (from *Nature*, 20–291) is a report by Captain Evans that Commander J. E. Pringle of H.M.S. *Vulture* had seen rapidly moving luminous waves or pulsations in the water. "On looking toward the east, that appearance was that of a revolving wheel with a center on that bearing, and whose spokes were illuminated, and, looking toward the west, a similar wheel appeared to be revolving, but in the opposite direction." (Commander Pringle considered the second wheel an optical illusion but was firm about the first one. He estimated the width of each shaft of light about 25 feet, the spaces between them about 100 feet. Duration of the phenomenon: about 35 minutes. Time: 9:40 P.M. Location: Lat. 26°26′N., Long. 53°11′E., in the Persian Gulf. The date was May 15, 1879.

Fort stated that the *Journal of the Royal Meteorological Society* (32–280) contained excerpts from a letter written by Mr. Douglas Carnegie saying that in 1906 he saw a bank of apparently quiet phosphorescence. But when the ship came close, "shafts of brilliant light came sweeping across the ship's bows . . . These light bars were about 20 feet apart and most regular . . . They first struck us on our broadside and I noticed that an intervening ship had no effect on the light beams: they started away from the lee sides of the ship just as if they had travelled right through it."

The place was the Gulf of Oman, the entrance to the Persian Gulf.

Fort has two more cases, one with the date of June 5,

1880, off the coast of Malabar and one with the date of March 14, 1907, in the Malacca Strait. The Malabar coast is the western coast of the Indian Peninsula, the direct continuation of the coastline which is the eastern shore of the Persian Gulf and the Gulf of Oman. The Malacca Strait is the water separating the Malay Peninsula from Sumatra. Because of subsequent developments I did not take the trouble to check the sources given by Fort. It is therefore possible that Fort, by condensing and shortening the reports, left out detail which to other eyes than his would have been significant. He does mention that Mr. Carnegie scooped up a bucket of water during the event and later examined samples under a microscope without finding anything unusual. He also mentions that Commander Pringle reported the sea "before and after the display" as having floating patches of fish spawn.

The "subsequent developments" just cited consisted in learning that a German scientist, Professor Dr. Kurt Kalle, had spent a long time collecting reports on this phenomenon that make a lasting impression on anybody who has ever seen it. Even sober logbook entries abound in terms like "weird," "most awe inspiring," "an effect of great eeriness," *unheimlich* (German for fear inspiring) and *angstwekkende indruk* (Dutch for fear inspiring). Even Dr. Kalle, who had only collected the reports, talked of *eine unheimliche Naturerscheinung*, a fear inspiring natural phenomenon. His summary appeared in the *Deutsche Hydrographische Zeitschrift* (vol. XIII, no. 2; April 1960), published by the German Hydrographic Institute. Dr. Kalle's sources were mainly *The Marine Observer*, published by Her Britannic Majesty's Stationary Office, plus some logbooks of German and Dutch vessels.[1]

[1] Professor Kalle's report does not contain any of the ones mentioned earlier in this chapter; but I have added these reports to his tabulation appearing in this chapter.

The total number of observations quoted by Dr. Kalle is seventy, but not all of them are about rotating luminous wheels. In going through all the reports of highly unusual phosphorescence in the sea that he could find he established several categories. At first these categories were merely to aid in sorting out, and were based on the described appearance of the phenomenon. Later, he found a very interesting and probably significant corollary. His first section, comprising six reports, he labelled "general and superficial descriptions," a somewhat harsh term, for some of them are impressive indeed. Besides I would have put three of these reports into the second section, which in Dr. Kalle's article consists of twenty-three reports.

These reports are all alike in that they describe what looks almost like an explosion. "Balls of light" suddenly appear at the ocean's surface, spreading out with utmost rapidity to cover an area of a hundred square yards or more. Here are a few examples of these reports:

The cargo ship *Stephan* was, on September 30, 1923, at 46° northern latitude and 15° western longitude, which is in the Atlantic Ocean to the west of the Bay of Biscay. The sea phosphoresced and "occasionally an extra brilliant patch would seem to bubble up from the bottom of the sea, burst into vivid light and spread rapidly over the surface before gradually fading away."

The captain of the S.S. *Omar* had a very similar story to tell. His ship was at 7°50′ N., 76°18′ E., which is in the Indian Ocean to the South of Ceylon; the date was October 14, 1923. "These patches of light, whilst expanding, became very brilliant and after about two minutes died away. They commenced with a diameter of about one foot and expanded to at least 30 yards."

Two years later, on August 23, 1925, the officer of the watch

(not named) of the German passenger liner *Preussen* produced the following description: "From right next to the ship and up to the limit of vision luminous balls rose from the lower strata of the ocean. Their distances from each other varied from 12 to 100 feet. The time interval between appearances varied between 20 and 30 seconds. The balls seemed to rise with a speed of about half a yard per second and had an estimated diameter of 8 inches. Just below the surface they expanded to a diameter of about half a yard. When reaching the surface these spheres expanded and flattened. It looked as if they were bursting. The area occupied by such a phantom body was ellipsoid in shape, with a major axis from 10 to 20 feet and a minor axis of 6 to 10 feet. The larger ones of them retained their intense silvery-greenish luminosity with a shivering motion until we lost sight of them." The location of the *Preussen* was also in the Indian Ocean, but to the west of that of the S.S. *Omar,* the precise position being 9° N., 63° East.

A little more than a year later, on October 31, 1926, S.S. *Somersetshire,* being in the same general area as the *Omar* and the *Preussen* (7°30′N., 74°30′E.) saw the same thing. P. H. Potter, the second officer, described it as "balls of brilliant light seemed to shoot from the depth, burst on nearing the surface, irradiate and cover an area, seemingly of a couple of hundred square yards."

Most of the reports of "exploding" balls of light come from the Indian Ocean, being strung out roughly along the 10th parallel of northern latitude from the African east coast to Ceylon's west coast.

Before I can go on to Dr. Kalle's surprising discovery, I have to list the categories he used. Category (A) is his six general descriptions. Category (B) is the twenty-three re-

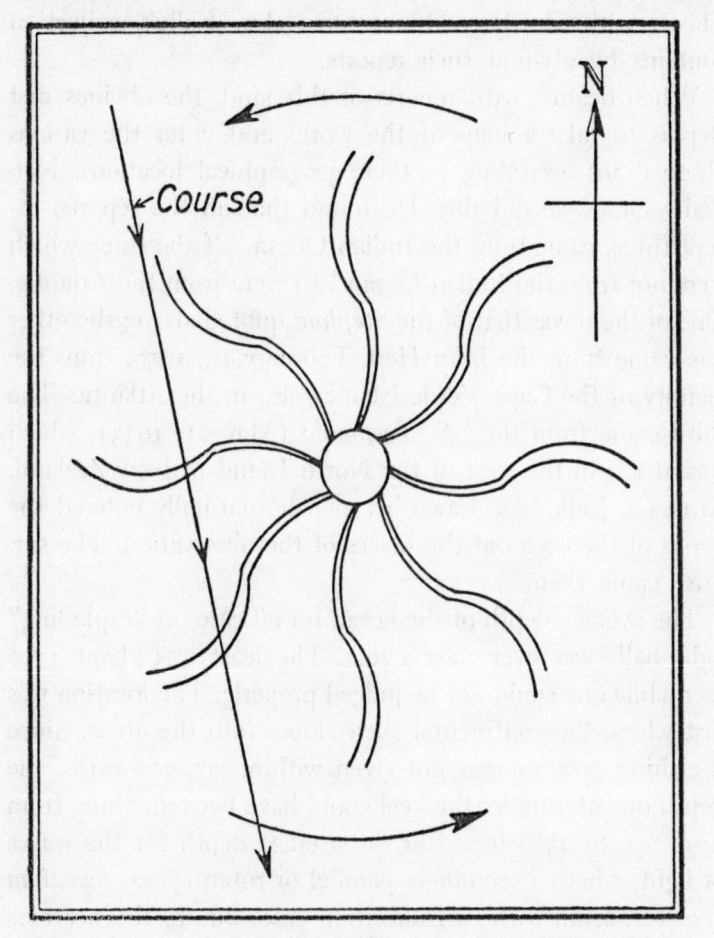

FIG. 16. Sketch made by an officer of the S.S. *Talma*. Observed December 28, 1929, northern part of the Andaman Sea.

ports on "exploding light balls," category (C) consists of eleven reports on waves of light, apparently parallel and not curved, moving across the surface, category (D) comprises seven reports about such waves that looked as if they were rotating around a center, but the center was not visible to the observer. The final category (E) deals with rotating

wheels with clearly visible centers. Dr. Kalle's collection contains twenty-four such reports.

When dealing with reports of this kind, the obvious first step is to take a map of the world and enter the various observations according to their geographical locations. Naturally Dr. Kalle did this. He found that all the reports, except three, came from the Indian Ocean. Of the three which were not from the Indian Ocean two were from the Atlantic. One of them was that of the *Stephan* quoted above; the other one came from the *John Holt*, February 19, 1957, from the vicinity of the Cape Verde Islands, also in the Atlantic. The third came from the S.S. *Tasmania* (May 21, 1933), which was at sea to the west of the North Island of New Zealand. After Dr. Kalle had drawn his map he naturally entered the depth of the ocean at the places of the observation. The surprise came then.

The average depth of the ocean for *all* cases of "exploding" light balls was over 10,000 feet. The least was about 1700 feet while one could not be judged properly. The location was just where the continental shelf slopes into the abyss. Since the ship's position was not given within, say, 200 yards, the depth of water under the keel could have been anything from from 700 to 3500 feet. But the average depth for the waves of light, whether seemingly parallel or rotating was *less than 300 feet*, again with two uncertain cases due to the nearness of the edge of the continental shelf.

The only definite exception as regards the freshly established rule of shallow water for parallel or rotating light beams was the S.S. *Somersetshire* on August 13, 1925. The position was 12°38′N., 55°28′E., which is not very far from the east coast of Africa. As a matter of fact I do not consider the report made by P. Hawkins, the second officer, very typical for the parallel light waves, since he wrote: "A white line

seemed to be coming toward the ship at a tremendous speed from the eastward, which had the appearance of breakers. Very shortly after, the whole sea was quite white, with now and again circular and streaky black patches, and the whole surroundings were brilliantly lightened up." But Hawkins added a very interesting comment: "During this time (9:20 P.M. till 10:40 P.M.) the atmospheric conditions were extraordinary. No sound was heard, not even the wind nor the breaking of the sea. No swell was visible; and the vessel, which had previously been rolling heavily, had practically no movement on her. In fact, one could almost have been in dock."

A far more typical report on the parallel waves was delivered by D. Brown, the second officer of the S.S. *City of Khios* on July 23, 1954. The ship was at 24°19′N., 66°20′E., in the northernmost part of the Arabian Sea, with a depth of water of about 200 feet. "Shafts of pale white light were observed moving swiftly NE–SW. They appeared to be just above the surface of the sea and parallel with each other. They were passing the ship at the rate of about one per second. They appeared to stretch as far as the eye could see on each side of the vessel and did not at any time appear to curve. After about 15 minutes the phenomenon disappeared."

While the experience of the S.S. *Somersetshire* must have been awe-inspiring, the case does not necessarily belong into this collection. If it be discarded as being "something else," whatever that may be, there is no exception to the rule found by Dr. Kalle that the exploding balls are a deep-water phenomenon, while the light beams appear only over the continental shelf. He himself wrote that "this result reinforces the supposition that the distinction into 'exploding' and 'ro-

tating' types, which was based on the differences in appearance and behavior, is essentially correct."

This fact is not very helpful in explaining either one of these phenomena. But in a field where observations (or at any event reports) have become reasonably frequent only during the last three decades, any definite fact is welcome. It may become important at a later date when more is known.

After quoting one more case of parallel light beams, because it contains an interesting guess, we can go on to the rotating beams. That case was reported by Captain Bradley of the S.S. *Aristo*. It was seen in July, 1938 (no date given) and the position of the vessel was 23°56′N., 66°53′E., quite close to the position of the S.S. *City of Khios*. "The beams," Captain Bradley wrote, "traveled in the reverse direction of the wind, sea and swell . . . The rapidly moving beams of luminosity may have been caused by minute phosphorescent organisms turning in a certain direction. Not that they moved rapidly from place to place, but that they remained practically stationary and only altered position to expose their luminous sides. Whatever the cause, the phenomenon was most awe-inspiring. No wonder that the mariners of old were so prone to superstition and returned to their native shores full of weird and wonderful tales of the sea."

The oldest report of rotating beams quoted by Dr. Kalle is dated May 23, 1906 and comes from the Gulf of Oman. The most interesting aspect is that it was observed from shore. The observer, a German by the name of A. Stürken, said that he was standing on board a ship which had made fast on a pier near Bender Abbas. The geographical position of the pier is given as 26°N., 57°E.

"The southern horizon was a luminous ribbon which looked precisely as if there were a heavy surf out there. The intensely bright luminescence approached us rapidly, shooting sharply

defined light rays to the West in rapid succession, looking like
the beam from the searchlight of a warship. Then the whole
luminous flood—always below the water's surface—approached
our ship. Wide waves of fire, 200 to 300 yards long, came in
endless succession and passed under our keel for a period of
about three minutes. Then the picture changed suddenly. To
the left of us, about 550 yards away, a gigantic fiery wheel
formed itself with spokes that reached as far as one could see.
The whole wheel whirled around for two or three minutes.
Then all of the luminescence moved away, as fast as it had
arrived. For a moment it was visible near the horizon and
then the apparition was over." (The word used by Stürken
which I translated as "apparition" is *Spuk*, normally used for
alleged supernatural phenomena, like seeing a ghost or witness-
ing Walpurgis Night.)

Most reports deal with the phenomenon when it is, if this
phrase is applicable here, in full bloom. Most of the time the
ship runs into a rotating wheel, or sees it some distance away.
But the crew of the S.S. *Aeneas* saw it develop. The date was
December 3, 1926; the place 5°48′ N., 98°9′ E., in the Strait
of Malacca, between Sumatra and the Malay Peninsula. The
report was written by J. M. Anderson, who was second officer
of the ship. The phenomenon began at 30 minutes after midnight:

"Commencing with but a few isolated points and patches
of sparkling and pulsating light, the display developed until
the surface of the sea from horizon to horizon had the appearance of being lit up from below, by thousands of beams
of light which independently flashed and were eclipsed with
great regularity, at intervals of about one second. This phosphorescence increased in brilliancy until 1:45 P.M. Two
distinct systems of light waves or phosphorescent wheels were
observed, one to port and one to starboard. These light waves

were observed to be traveling clockwise over the surface of the sea, appearing to issue from a focus around which they rotated, increasing in brilliancy and velocity of rotation until 2:05 A.M. The phosphorescent points and patches previously described were noticed to increase in brilliancy as the illuminated beams swept over them and to decrease in intensity during the passage of the successive dark spaces, and this phenomenon was quite noticeable even when the light waves, toward the end of the display, became quite faint. At 2:15 A.M. the light waves were no longer visible, and at 2:30 A.M. the last traces of phosphorescence were observed."

The crew of the S.S. *Arracan*, on December 19, 1927, being in the same general area (14°23′N., 96°3′E.) also watched the development of a rather short-lived phenomenon. At 2 A.M. the vessel passed "through small clusters of phosphorescent light." Very soon after, "these clusters of light expanded into bars and commenced to revolve in an anticlockwise direction, and appeared to pass the bridge, from where they were observed, at the rate of one every half second. This phenomenon was in the form of a Catherine wheel, the hub of which could be observed plainly about two hundred yards to the westward of the ship's course. At 2:05 A.M. the phosphorescent light failed, and then became brighter, and on this occasion the spokes or beams of light revolved in the opposite direction, i.e. clockwise. At 2:15 A.M. this phenomenon disappeared. On each occasion the hub of the Catherine wheel was clearly visible to the westward of the ship."

Quite close to the position of the S.S. *Arracan*, namely at 14°15′N., 96°41′E., and almost precisely two years later, namely on December 28, 1929, the S.S. *Talma* also observed a rotating wheel. The "spokes" were curved (as in Fig. 16) and about 30 feet wide when they hit the ship. The "spokes" followed each other at intervals of half a second. The hub of

the wheel, which could not be seen very clearly, seemed to be about five miles from the ship. The duration of the whole was 15 minutes. This report has an interesting postscript: "It was later reported from the engine room that at this time the revolutions [of the engine] dropped considerably and the main engines were straining. As this straining of the engines appeared to me to point to the possibility of a marine volcanic disturbance I considered it advisable to send out a wireless warning."

It would serve little purpose to quote more reports. They all read more or less alike and all stress the weird impressiveness of the sight—quite naturally, since for each observer it was the first time that he saw it. One exception to that rule is the experience of Captain R. W. White and his second officer, C. Jackman, who saw it three times, on September 9, October 5 and December 29, 1932. The location for all three observations was the Andaman Sea and Second Officer Jackman, on the third occasion, merely entered: "Experienced the same phenomenon, duration 26 minutes." Well, one can also get used even to being under artillery bombardment, as many soldiers can testify.

Geographically the phenomenon of the rotating lights clearly centers around two areas. The first one is the Gulf of Aden, the Persian Gulf and the Gulf of Oman, plus the coastline to the East of the Gulf of Oman to about Bombay. The other area is the sea around the Malay Peninsula, the Andaman Sea, the Strait of Malacca and the Borneo Sea.

For simplicity's sake I referred to these two areas as the Western and the Eastern Phenomenon and, trying to see whether the seasons (admittedly not too noticeable in these tropical seas) had anything to do with the frequency of occurrence, I tabulated all reports as to their dates. (See table.)

TABLE OF SEASONAL FREQUENCY OF OBSERVATIONS

		Western Phenomenon	Eastern Phenomenon
		Number of Observations	
JANUARY	first half	—	—
	second half	1	—
FEBRUARY	first half	—	—
	second half	—	2
MARCH	first half	—	1
	second half	2	—
APRIL	first half	2	—
	second half	—	2
MAY	first half	3	—
	second half	1	2
JUNE	first half	—	1
	second half	2	1
JULY	first half	2	—
	second half	2	1
AUGUST	first half	1	1
	second half	—	—
SEPTEMBER	first half	1	2
	second half	1	—
OCTOBER	first half	—	1
	second half	—	2
NOVEMBER	first half	2	4
	second half	1	1
DECEMBER	first half	—	1
	second half	—	3

It can be seen that the Western Phenomenon shows a rather faint clustering for the period from late March to the end of July, while the Eastern Phenomenon shows a somewhat more pronounced clustering for the period from October through December. But, since neither clustering is very pronounced, it might be argued that the apparent concentration during the last three months of the year for the Eastern

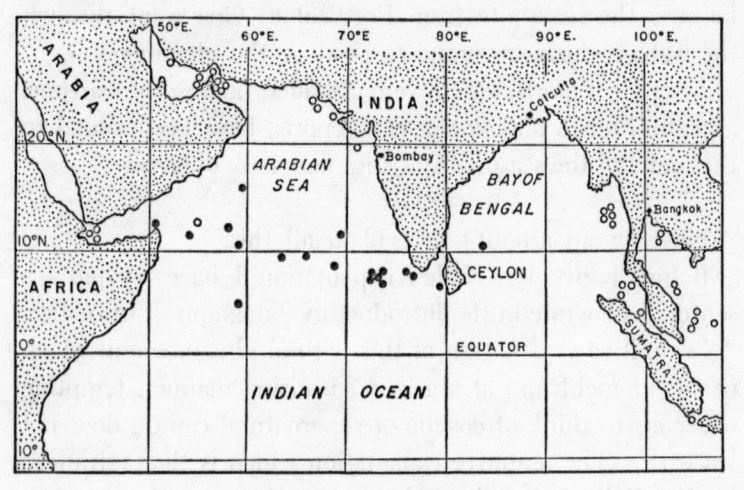

FIG. 17. The northern portion of the Indian Ocean, showing the area where the mysterious luminous phenomena have been seen. Circles indicate rotating luminescences, black spots show the places where "exploding balls of light" were seen. (Only reports after 1900 have been used for this map.)

Phenomenon is caused by the simple fact that the number of reports is not large enough to be meaningful. Dr. Kalle has a total of only five reports for the years from 1906 to 1914. Then there is a complete absence of reports for the years 1915 to 1919, caused, no doubt, by the first World War. There is the same absence of reports for the years from 1939 to 1949, caused by the second World War and its aftermath. No doubt quite a number of reports from those years do exist but, since they formed part of otherwise classified material, were never published. And so far the collection is somewhat limited also to nationality. Reports from British vessels seem to be known more or less completely, thanks to *The Marine Observer*, and some reports from Dutch vessels have appeared in the Dutch marine publication *De Zee*. Nobody, so far, has gone over the material that might be hiding in French and Portuguese publications. I expect the latter especially to yield much material

because the sea route from Portugal to Goa went through the waters which are prone to produce the phenomenon.

After the reports which were classified because of wartime, and the French and Portuguese reports, have been added to the material the seasonal statistics may look different.

Now for an attempt to explain all this.

Before I give Dr. Kalle's explanation I have to quote a sentence he wrote in the introductory paragraph of his paper: "A definitive explanation of this natural phenomenon, which occurs at night and at sea in a surprising manner, tempting observers to think of cosmic or supernatural causes, does not yet exist." The tentative explanation which is then advanced by Dr. Kalle is based on the known fact that luminescent marine organisms do not luminesce all the time. If they did, we would have phosphorescence all the time. But when the sea does phosphoresce it can clearly be seen that the organisms repond to physical stimuli. No captain of a sailing vessel ever produced as bright a wake as do the propellers of a steamer or motor ship. And if you stand in shallow water when there is phosphorescence you can produce an extra bright flash by the simple expedient of striking the surface with your outstretched hand.

The small organisms—they are not actually microscopic, as one can read in many places, since the most common one measures about a millimeter in diameter—definitely respond to the shock wave produced by the blow on the surface.

That they also seem to respond to something we don't even feel is shown by the report of the ship's master of the M.S. *British Premier* (Nov. 30, 1951; location: southern portion of the Persian Gulf): "The ship's radar apparatus had been switched on with a view to checking her position, when, in the same instant this gear became operative, most brilliant

boomerang-shaped arcs of phosphorescent light appeared in the sea, gyrating in a clockwise direction to starboard and anticlockwise to port, but all sweeping inward toward the ship."

Now since the luminescence can be excited by a stimulus it is, as Captain Bradley of the S.S. *Aristo* pointed out, not necessary that the organisms themselves move rapidly. A rapidly moving stimulus would produce the same appearance. Professor Kalle thinks that shock waves provide this stimulus, the shock waves themselves being caused by submarine earthquakes.

The rotating wheels, according to the same theory, might be caused by the interference of shock waves from two different sources, of which the second might be a reflection of the first. Dr. Kalle places some emphasis on this thought.

The validity of the whole explanation depends on a rapid "lights on, light off" of the organisms involved. If they, once stimulated, continued to luminesce for a few minutes, one would only get a generally luminous sea from seismic shock waves, but no definite figures. The next point of the investigation clearly lies in the field of marine biology. For it has to be established just what organism, or organisms, accounts for most of the phosphorescence in the areas involved. Then it has to be established whether they respond to shock waves. That they will seems likely, but it might need the presence of another condition to make them respond. Finally it has to be established whether they "switch off" quickly after the stimulus.

Once the answers to all three questions have been found, it should be possible to make a mathematical analysis comparing the speed of shock waves underwater with the observed velocities of motion of the luminous waves.

I have one more question in mind: has there ever been a

naval battle after dark in one of these areas? And if so, did the shell splashes cause light waves, wheels and counter-wheels?

If so, shouldn't it be possible to cause a "Wheel of Poseidon" by means of underwater explosions? If that could be done the wheel would not come as a surprise, but could be produced when everything is ready for its study.

CHAPTER VIII

STRANGE PLANET NEXT DOOR

THERE IS A STRANGE PLANET of which only a little is known so far. It cannot be visited by explorers unless they are encased in a massive steel hull, and all the time they have to stay inside they cannot even open a window.

And even this possibility is a recent achievement. Before that it could be explored only remotely by way of probes that succeeded in capturing outlandish life forms adapted to an "impossible" environment. The facts known about it so far are as follows:

The pressure at the surface is several hundred times the pressure which humans consider normal; in some places, it goes up to a thousand times normal. The temperature is to all intents and purposes the same, regardless of latitude, time of day or season. What variations there are are minor, amounting to two or three degrees, with the average hovering some five degrees above the freezing point of water. Likewise there are no changes in illumination, regardless of time of day or season. Surprisingly, the abundance of life-forms is simply fantastic, both in number of individuals and in the number of different life-forms. At unknown intervals—seasonally?—long-lasting and very dense mud winds are blowing, presumably changing local topography to a very large extent.

This is not a description of a planet circling a remote sun, conceived by a science fiction writer with a superior knowl-

edge of possible environments. It is a description of a real and otherwise rather well-known planet, at least of about half of it. It is the planet next door to us—the bottom of the ocean.

Oceanography is a rather young science, not quite as young, of course, as nuclear physics or space medicine, but young just the same. This may sound surprising in view of the fact that people have been sailing the seas for thousands of years, that tribes and nations made their living by catching fish and that for many centuries trade and sailing were virtually synonymous terms. Fact is, however, that until about a century ago the study of the seas was literally superficial. What happened below about 20 fathoms, the greatest depth to which fishing nets were lowered, was of no interest to anybody. The currents the sailors were interested in were surface currents. The swarming of fish which interested the fisherman was surface swarming.

People still speak of the abyss when they refer to the ocean beyond the sight of land. The word itself means "bottomless" and is Low Latin of Greek derivation. No modern man would believe it to be strictly true, but for a long time sailors thought that the high seas were actually bottomless. We know this mostly because a seventeenth-century geographer, Bernard Varenius of Hanover, devoted several pages of type to a refutation of this belief.

In this refutation, he unearthed an opinion from classical antiquity which stated that the world was symmetrical, which meant that the greatest deeps of the ocean should be equal to the highest mountains on land. I may remark in passing that this old guess is very nearly correct. After Varenius, everybody was convinced that there had to be an ocean bottom somewhere.

Beginning about a hundred and fifty years ago, some scientists went to work on a few problems. One of the first was to measure temperature. The results looked curiously alike. In the arctic oceans, the surface water was near freezing and stayed that way as far as the thermometers of that time could go down. In the tropical seas, it was nice and warm for the first score of feet or so. Then it got cooler, and as soon as the thermometer went below 100 fathoms (600 feet to land-lubbers), there didn't seem to be much difference between arctic and tropical measurements.

A Frenchman by the name of Péron drew what looked like a logical conclusion: if you went still deeper, the temperature would, at one still-to-be-determined level, drop to below freezing point. The bottoms of the oceans were, without any doubt whatsoever, covered with ice.

Naturally there would be no life on these ice-covered bottoms, partly because it was too cold, partly because there was nothing to eat. Logically, too, the ice was likely to begin at a shallower level in the Arctic, although this would still have to be determined. It was not really encouraging to this theory that Sir John Ross, one day in 1818, accidentally caught a brittle star at a probable depth of 4900 feet—in Baffin Bay in the Arctic.

The brittle star received the scientific name of *Gorgonocephalus* and was then quickly forgotten. If somebody had brought the case up again, he probably would have been told that the fact that Sir John Ross had found a depth of 4900 feet at that spot, coupled with the fact that the creature had become entangled in the line, still did not prove that it came from the bottom. It could have become entangled at any depth.

During the early part of the nineteenth century, an Englishman, Edward Forbes, did very diligent work on life in the

seas, at first in the North Sea and the English Channel, later in the Mediterranean. He pointed out that marine plants needed sunlight, like any other plants. Up to a depth of about 45 fathoms, plant life was abundant, but then quickly became rare as the light began to fail. (Later researchers put the lower limit of active plant life at 175 fathoms.) But where there was no plant life, there could be no animal life; below the level of 1800 feet, or 300 fathoms, there had to be a zone that was not populated, could not be populated. This was Edward Forbes' *Abyssus Theory*, advanced in 1843 and based on his own very careful and very thorough researches in an "abysmal region" of the Mediterranean Sea.

Very few scientific theories had such a short and unhappy life as Forbes' *Abyssus Theory*. A Norwegian zoologist, Pastor Michael Sars, who as a young man and while *candidatus theologiae* had made important discoveries about the sex life and the metamorphosis of marine mollusks, started fishing near the Lofoten Islands in the summer of 1850, assisted by his 15-year-old son Johan Ernst. Pastor Sars not only obtained living things from a depth of 450 fathoms, he obtained living things that were supposed to be tropical. Or else extinct. They were a crinoid, *Rhizocrinus lofotensis* (Fig. 18), a representative of one of the four main groups of the echinoderms.

Everybody knows some echinoderms, even if he has never heard the name. The common sea star is the typical representative of one of the main groups. The well-known sea urchin is a representative of the second one, and the sea cucumber represents the third. The fourth group, the sea lilies or crinoids, were thought to be extinct.

But then, in 1755, a naturalist received something that had been dredged from the sea not far from Martinique. It was called *Pentacrinus caput Medusae* (if you insist on a translation, it would come out as "the Medusa-headed five-sectioned

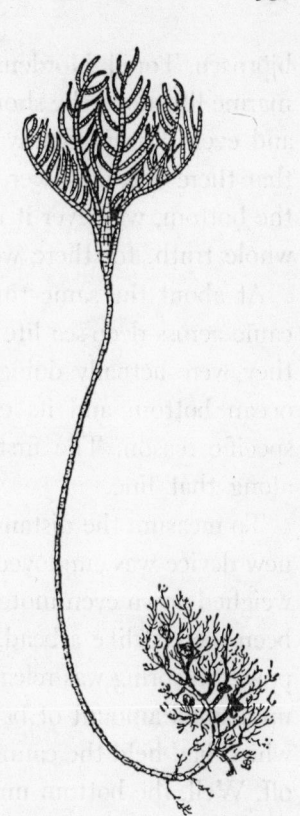

FIG. 18. *Rhizocrinus lofotensis*, living crinoid discovered in 1850 at depth of 450 fathoms. Illustration copied from Pastor Sars's original report. The animal is about 4 inches tall.

something"), but it took a quarter of a century until the anatomist Johann Friedrich Blumenbach proved that it was an echinoderm. For many years, it was considered the only surviving species of the type. For many more years, it was considered incredibly rare; as late as 1890, a naturalist had to part with eleven golden "sovereigns" for a specimen. The history of *Pentacrinus* at least enabled Pastor Sars to tell at once what it was he had caught.

Pastor Sars had started something. A whole swarm of Scandinavian marine biologists with names like Lovén, As-

NOTE. The illustrations in this chapter were drawn by Olga Ley, unless credited otherwise.

björnsen, Torell, Nordenskjöld, Lindahl and Théel went after marine life along the shorelines of Norway, Sweden, Svalbard, and even Novaya Semlyá, and were unanimous in reporting that there was no lower limit for marine life. The limit was the bottom, wherever it might be, and even that was not the whole truth, for there were forms *in* the bottom mud.

At about the same time, English and American scientists came across deep-sea life without, at first, meaning to. What they were actually doing was determining the depth of the ocean bottom and its contours along a specific line for a specific reason. The first transatlantic cable was to be laid along that line.

To measure the distance from the surface to the bottom, a new device was employed. It consisted of a heavy metal pipe, weighed down even more by a large iron cannon ball that had been pierced like a bead. When the pipe touched bottom, a powerful spring was released which did two things: it scooped up a small amount of bottom mud, and it released the catch which had held the cannon ball in place so that it would slip off. Well, the bottom mud contained animal remains, regardless of place and depth.

The first transatlantic cable was laid in 1858, but it worked for only three months. The next one, laid in 1865, broke when about two-thirds finished. The one of 1866 was successful. Then the broken end of the 1865 cable was fished up and the laying completed after repair. The important thing was that the broken end of the 1865 cable brought animal life with it to the surface. By one of these coincidences that happen more often than one should suppose, the cable across the Mediterranean (from Sardinia to Algiers) broke at about the same time. It was fished up too, and at a portion which had been at nearly 10,000 feet for only three years, fifteen

different kinds of animal life were found—right in the sea for which Forbes had originally evolved his *Abyssus Theory*.

The man responsible, either directly or by his example, for everything that was to follow was Professor (later Sir) Wyville Thomson of Edinburgh. Pastor Michael Sars had not only proved that there was abundant animal life in the "abyss" of the northern seas, he had even found animals best known from the geological past. Wasn't it time for Her Majesty's Government to do something about it? The Royal Society, represented by its vice president Professor Carpenter, chimed in and Her Majesty's Government finally put two small vessels of the Royal Navy, the *Lightning* and the *Porcupine*, at Wyville Thomson's disposal. They investigated the sea bottom around England, off the Spanish coast and in the Mediterranean.

It might be remarked here that the hopes of some of the scientists were off on a wrong track for a number of years to come, largely due to the accident that the first major discovery made by Pastor Sars had been a crinoid. Crinoids were regarded as virtually a signature of the geologic past (right now, a monograph on *The Living Crinoids* is being published; it has so many volumes that I have lost track) and it seemed quite possible that "the abyssal life" was a "Lost World"—the bottom of the Atlantic might be the bottom of a Jurassic ocean. We now know that it isn't so, and it is still slightly surprising that it isn't, but that wrong hope was a strong spur.

Following the success of the *Porcupine* and the *Lightning*, Wyville Thomson asked for more help and got it. On December 21, 1872, the corvette *Challenger* left England for a trip which covered all the oceans except the Arctic Ocean. When the *Challenger* berthed in Portsmouth again on May 26, 1876, she had spent 719 days at sea, traveled a total of

68,890 nautical miles, measured the depth of the ocean, beyond those areas already on nautical charts, in 370 points, measured bottom temperatures in 275 places, collected 600 crates of specimens (among them a bottom-mud sample from a depth of 27,000 feet from the Pacific Ocean near the Philippines) and used up the original budget of 100,000 pounds. Another 68,000 pounds had to be spent just for the publication of the results.

Like naturally begets like. If the Queen of England could send Sir Wyville Thomson and his assistant Sir John Murray to explore the bottom of the seas, the United States could do the same. Professor Alexander Agassiz got the *Blake* to investigate, in successive trips, the Gulf of Mexico, the Caribbean Sea and the Atlantic Coast of the United States. Later, the United States sent the *Albatross* into the Pacific.

And if *Her* Majesty's Government could spend 100,000 pounds on such an idealistic cause, *His* Majesty's Government (that of the Kaiser of Germany, that is) could do the same. On July 31, 1898, the steamer *Valdivia* left the harbor of Hamburg as the official German deep-sea expedition, commanded by Captain Adalbert Krech, under the scientific leadership of Professor Carl Chun, and sent off in person by the then Secretary of the Interior Count von Posadowsky. The successor to Sir Wyville Thomson, Sir John Murray, was on board for the first leg of the trip, from Hamburg to Edinburgh.

With that noted, let's go back to the *Challenger* expedition. Soon after the *Challenger*'s return to England, the scientific world began to scatter references to foraminifers and radiolarians in interviews and popular articles so that they very nearly became household words. I suspect that in many households, nobody had too clear an idea of just what foraminifers and radiolarians really were, but the terms *were* popu-

lar. Both refer to single-celled animals much like the better-known ameba. But while the ameba is naked, the others grow armor. The shell of the foraminifers is calcareous (chalky) and most of the time resembles a tiny snail shell.

Considering that they are single-celled, the foraminifers are quite large (Fig. 19). Single specimens of all of them are just

FIG. 19. *Polystomella strigillata*, a foraminifer. Magnified 250 times.

visible to the naked eye if put on a contrasting background. One living form has a shell 1/20th of an inch in diameter. A few fossil forms grew to a size of nearly an inch.

The radiolarians are also single-celled and much smaller than the foraminifers, and their shells (also called "skele-

tons," which I find slightly misleading) are of silica. In shape, they do not follow a specific pattern, though lacy spheres of various types are frequent, but they are all beautiful.

The reason why the *Challenger* expedition popularized these names is that their many samples of deep-sea bottom mud fell into three general classifications, namely "globigerina ooze" (*globigerina* is the most common of the foraminifers), "radiolarian ooze" and "red ooze." Each was typical for a certain depth. Near the shores, the bottom sediments for a few hundred miles out consist mostly of dry-land stuff, sand and clay and soil washed into the sea by the rivers. Then away from the land and farther down comes the gray bottom mud consisting of globigerina shells; we now know that 30 per cent of the ocean floor (amounting to 40 million square miles) is covered with globigerina ooze.

In samples from more than 12,000 feet in depth, the *Challenger* scientists found that globigerina shells became rare and soon were lacking altogether. A theory for this was thought up at once.

The *Challenger* experts assumed that the foraminifers did not live at the bottom but floated freely at shallow depths. This assumption was correct. When the individual died, the shell sank to the bottom, but below the 12,000-foot level, the sea water, being under enormous pressure, contained enough carbon dioxide to dissolve the calcareous shells. But this chemical action would not attack the silica shells of the radiolarians, so there you got radiolarian ooze. (We know of three million square miles of radiolarian ooze in the Indian and Pacific Oceans.) And the extreme deep sea also yielded "red ooze" which, it could be determined quickly, was mostly volcanic dust, often containing tiny spheres, on the order of 1/100th of an inch or less in diameter, micro-meteorites.

Of all this, the radiolarians most strongly took the public

fancy, no doubt because of the appearance of their skeletons. And it so happened that these radiolarians had a special scientific history which not only made interesting reading but was full of the most famous names in contemporary science.

During the whole interval from Forbes' *Abyssus Theory* to the *Challenger* expedition, there was one scientist who was *the* authority on microscopic animals. He was Christian Gottfried Ehrenberg in Berlin. He was born in 1795 and died at the age of 81 in the year that the *Challenger* expedition returned home.

Ehrenberg probed endlessly into stagnant water, into dust, mud and ground-up rock and the whole world helped him. An American sent him the first deep-sea mud samples ever taken. That American was Matthew Fontaine Maury, at one time Superintendent of the Naval Observatory and later called the Father of Oceanography. It was Maury who had helped in the survey prior to laying the first transatlantic cable.

In Maury's samples, Ehrenberg discovered the radiolarians, though he did not give them that name. Then Ehrenberg received rock samples from the island of Barbados, packed masses of radiolarian skeletons. He concluded that the radiolarians probably lived at the bottom of the deep sea, and he never expected to see a live one. He didn't, but this was largely his fault.

Scientists have often been accused of keeping their noses buried in books and journals and neglecting nature. Ehrenberg had the opposite fault: he kept his eye glued to his microscope and did not keep up with professional literature. It must be admitted that it would have needed a kind of literary detective at first.

An obscure ship's doctor on the run from England to Aus-

tralia (on H.M.S. *Rattlesnake*) fished little lumps of a jelly-like substance from the ocean in 1851. His microscope told him that these lumps were colonies of single-celled animals, each one having a most beautiful skeleton. The ship's doctor was the later very famous Thomas Huxley, Darwin's friend. He also had failed to follow the literature (understandable for a ship's doctor of his time) and did not know about Ehrenberg's finds in Maury's mud samples.

The next famous name in the story was that of Professor Johannes Müller. He had seen such tiny strands of jelly in 1849 but paid no attention until he read Huxley's report in 1855. Then, really going to work on them, he almost drowned off the coast of Norway in pursuit of radiolarians. But he invented the name, and he influenced one of his pupils who had exceptional artistic talent to continue these studies. The name of his pupil was Ernst Haeckel, who began his researches near Messina in 1859. In 1862, the first book devoted to the radiolarians was published, a folio volume of 572 pages of print with 35 plates of copper engravings (Fig. 20). Other zoologists felt that Ernst Haeckel had exhausted the theme with this volume. This probably was more or less true at the moment.

But then the *Challenger* expedition came home. While still *en route*, the men of the *Challenger* had made microscope slides and decided that all mud containing more than 20 per cent radiolarian skeletons should be labeled radiolarian ooze. Of course somebody had to work this material. The aging and ailing Sir Wyville Thomson discussed this with his friend Sir John Murray. Their opinion was unanimous: Ernst Haeckel. Haeckel was invited to England; he accepted the offer, saying that it would take him three years, possibly as long as five years. It took ten.

It also took three volumes, totaling 2750 pages with 140

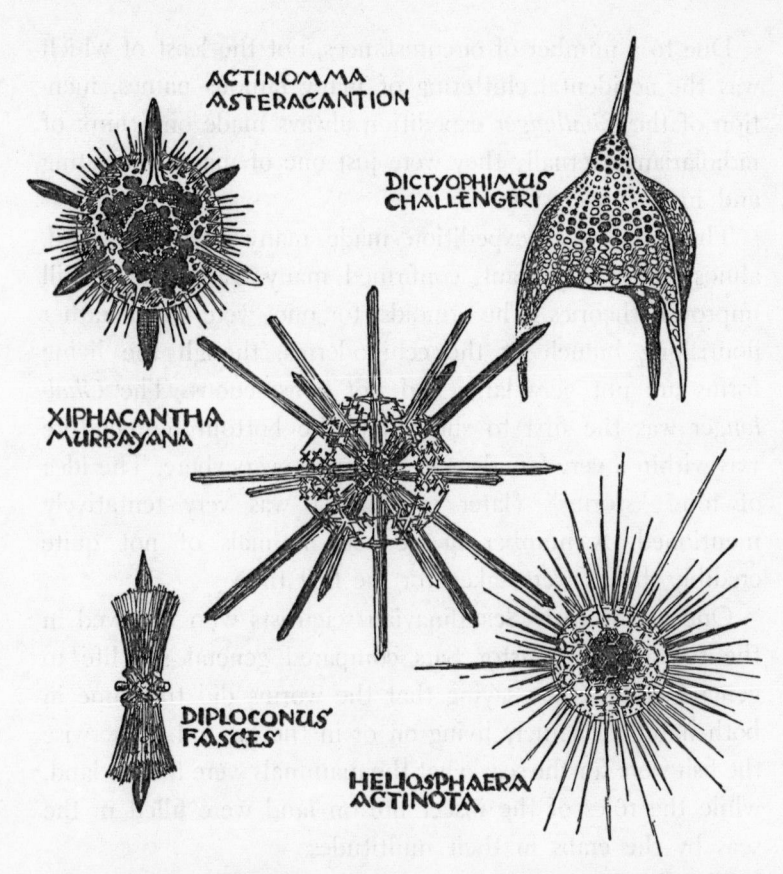

ACTINOMMA
ASTERACANTION

DICTYOPHIMUS
CHALLENGERI

XIPHACANTHA
MURRAYANA

DIPLOCONUS
FASCES

HELIOSPHAERA
ACTINOTA

FIG. 20. Five radiolarians discovered by Ernst Haeckel. Drawn from Haeckel's original report by the late Professor Gustav Wolf.

plates, to describe just the radiolarians. (These three volumes were labeled "Part XVIII" of the Challenger Report.) Haeckel's teacher Müller had known 50 different species. In Haeckel's monograph of 1862, another 144 species were added. The *Challenger* discovered 3508 additional new species. Haeckel later said that his enthusiasm never abated, but that it strained his imagination to invent 3500 new scientific names!

Due to a number of circumstances, not the least of which was the accidental cluttering of many famous names, mention of the *Challenger* expedition always made one think of radiolarians. Actually they were just one of many interesting and important results.

The *Challenger* expedition made many discoveries and, almost more important, confirmed many reasonable if still unproven theories. The crinoids, for one, were still a rather flourishing branch of the echinoderms, though the living forms are not very large and not conspicuous. The *Challenger* was the first to show that the bottom temperature was within a very few degrees the same everywhere. The idea of mud "storms" (later confirmed) was very tentatively mentioned. A number of deep-sea animals of not quite credible shapes were taken for the first time.

One of the early Scandinavian scientists who followed in the footsteps of Pastor Sars compared general sea life to general land life by saying that the worms did the same in both habitats, namely living on or in the ground. Otherwise the fish were for the seas what the mammals were for the land, while the rôles of the insect life on land were filled in the seas by the crabs in their multitudes.

The *Challenger* results could say "yes" to this idea and add "anywhere and at any depth." But this nice comparison omitted something very typical for the sea. On land, the only thing that does not move around are the plants. The plants of the seas do not move either, but in the ocean there are very many animals which also don't move: oysters and all their relatives, sponges, corals, sea anemones and so forth.

Originally, the rather natural tendency had been to sort ocean life according to the depth where it lived; after the *Challenger* returned, another sorting method triumphed, the

sorting into the three categories called *Benthos*, *Nekton* and *Plankton*.

Benthos is everything that does not move (except in juvenile stages) and it includes the true plants (algae) as well as corals, barnacles, sea anemones, sponges, plus those which, while able to move, do not normally do so, like seastars, sea urchins and many worms.

The *Nekton* comprises everything that moves actively: almost all fishes, whales, the larger octopi. The *Plankton* comprises the passively moving forms which drift with the currents. Most of the life-forms of the *Plankton* happen to be tiny, while those of the *Nekton* are usually large.[1]

This division according to habits, if they may be called that, sounds at first hearing like the subdivisions of primitive zoology of the sixteenth century, where everything living was divided into "animals with feet," "animals with fins" and "animals with wings." But in the seas there is not just one but a variety of reasons for sorting first into habits, then into habitats and finally into a proper zoological classification.

Well, what happened to the charming idea that the abysmal zone might harbor a "lost world"? It happens not to be true. Of course there are so-called living fossils in the ocean. One can make the sweeping and, to a layman, rather surprising statement that all the sharks could be considered as living fossils, since they are a very old group of the vertebrates. But most sharks are pelagic surface swimmers, though deep-sea forms are known. And one of the very oldest living fossils is *Limulus*, the horseshoe crab, a rather familiar creature to

[1] The oft-used term "pelagic" just means "of the (open) sea" as distinct from "littoral," which means "near the shore," specifically the area uncovered at low tide. "Pelagic" then comprises both *Nekton* and *Plankton*, provided it is far from the shore.

Americans along the Atlantic coast, but a much-admired survivor from the dim geologic past to people elsewhere. Far from being a deep-sea form, it is an animal of the littoral zone.

Only one group of crabs, the so-called eryonids, fits the idea of living fossils from the abyss. These eryonids were known fossils from Jurassic sediments—about 180 million years old—and they were then definitely inhabitants of the littoral zone. Naturally they were believed to be extinct, until the *Challenger* expedition fished some from the deep sea off Africa. They do not differ much from their Jurassic an-

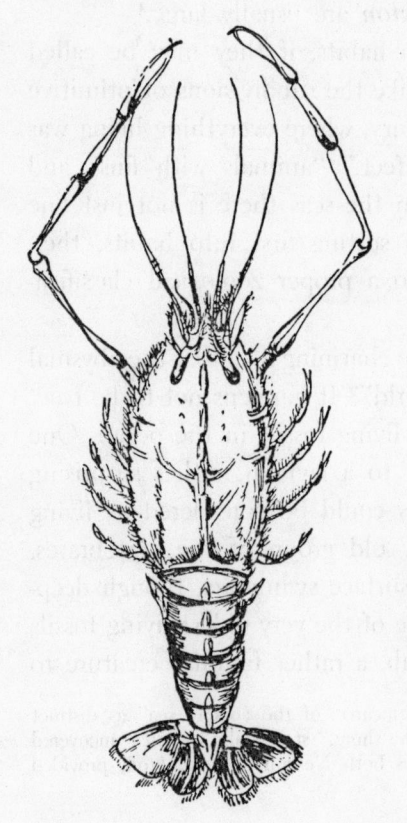

FIG. 21. *Willemoesia leptodactyla*, one of the "extinct" eryonids discovered by *Challenger* expedition.

cestors except that they have lost their eyes in the meantime. Of course we can't tell how the Jurassic eryonids were colored; the living forms have bright red claws, feelers, legs and tail, while the body is the color of light pink chalk (see Fig. 21).

Within a single century, scientific opinion about the bottom of the ocean had undergone fundamental revisions three times. The ice-covered bottom was disproved first, the idea that the ocean bottom was without life had to go next and its "replacement," namely that it was a repository of ancient life forms, was disproved by the *Challenger* expedition. The seas harbor fewer "living fossils" than the land areas, though a few of them, discovered only recently, are of high age and consequently of great scientific interest, indeed.

The next major voyage of exploration was that of the German vessel *Valdivia*, twenty-two years later. Of course there had been other oceanographic journeys. The American vessel *Tuscarora* had investigated the seas near Japan, during the same years the *Challenger* made its voyage. During the years 1876–78 the Norwegian vessel *Vøringen* under the scientific leadership of H. Mohn and G. D. Sars investigated the sea bottom of the high north, while the French expeditions of the *Travailleur,* beginning in 1880, paid attention to the sea bottom of the Gulf of Biscay, the area between Spain and the Canary Islands and the western Mediterranean. At the same time the Prince of Monaco, with the *Hirondelle,* personally undertook scientific voyages in the Mediterranean and the Atlantic to the Azores. (Later, in 1898, he went to the Arctic Ocean with the *Princesse Alice II.*) The Austrians, beginning in 1890, used the *Pola* to investigate the eastern portion of the Mediterranean and, after finding that this area was not too productive from the zoological point of view, extended their activities to the Red Sea.

But the *Valdivia* expedition was a world-wide expedition,

with special emphasis on the Indian Ocean, which had been somewhat neglected by the *Challenger*. The scientific chief of the expedition, Professor Carl Chun, and his fellow scientists on board had the advantage that they, between them, had read all the fifty quarto volumes that reported the work of the *Challenger*. They knew what had been done wrong or awkwardly on that first try. New and better nets and other equipment had been designed and constructed in the meantime. Consequently the *Valdivia* expedition did as well as the *Challenger* expedition in a shorter time.

There was another improvement too. The *Challenger* expedition had lost over a dozen men, not because of accidents but due to heat prostration, tropical diseases and plain exhaustion. The *Valdivia* lost only one man—ironically he was the ship's doctor.

Leaving Hamburg on July 31, 1898, the first stop of the voyage was Edinburgh to bring Sir John Murray home. After a short stop the *Valdivia* sailed around Scotland and Ireland, then took course due south for the Canary Islands and more or less followed the African coast. From Capetown, course was SSW for the purpose of finding Bouvet Island if they could (they did), then east to Enderby Land on the coast of Antarctica, from there up to Sumatra, then across the Indian Ocean to Dar-es-Salaam in East Africa, then north along the African coast to the Red Sea. Then the *Valdivia* sailed the whole length of the Mediterranean Sea and around Spain back to Hamburg, which was reached on April 28, 1899.

A member of the expedition recalled later that one of the first questions asked of him by a newspaper reporter was: "Did you catch any monsters of the deep?" The scientist replied that they had caught monsters all right, but that the reporter would not agree, so let's call them bathypelagic fishes. To understand this exchange, it must be explained

that the German word for monster is *Ungeheuer*, but the adjective *ungeheuerlich* mostly means "gigantic."

They were "monsters," yes, but they were little. One of my childhood memories is myself standing in front of the displays in the Museum of Natural History in Berlin and marveling at the monsters. Why, they were all of so small a size that one could easily keep them in a fish tank at home! Building a fish tank which could actually do that would be a major engineering task. It would cost, I guess, around $15,000 and would still have the considerable disadvantage of not letting you see what's going on inside.

There were two small black misshapen fishes, each about

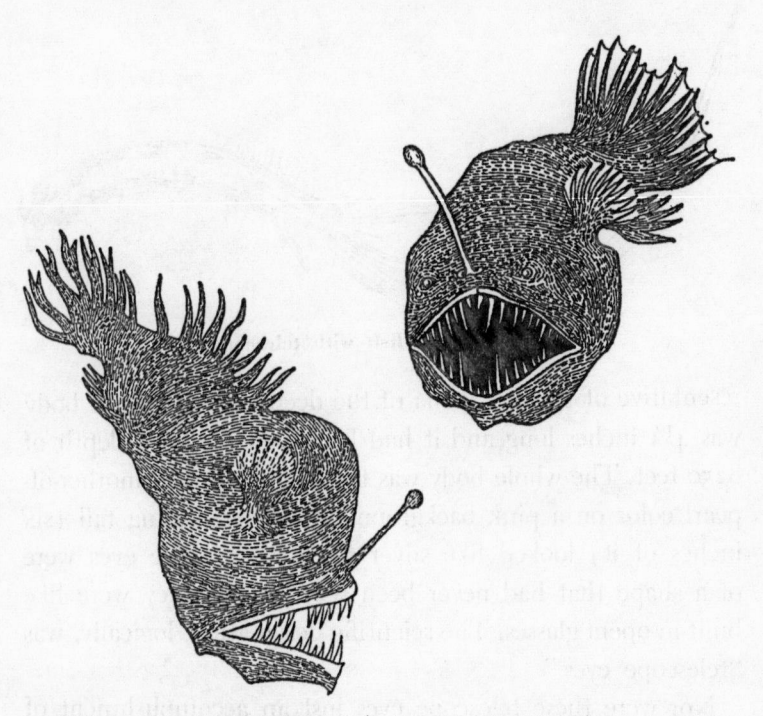

FIG. 22. *Melanocetus johnsoni* (left) and *Melanocetus krechi* (right).

three inches long (Fig. 22). Your first impression was that
this was mainly a mouth. The teeth, though tiny, still looked
both vicious and, strange to say, luminous. These two fishes,
one taken in the Atlantic at a depth of 13,500 feet, the
other in the Indian Ocean at a similar depth, had come up
still alive and had lived on board the *Valdivia* for about an
hour. They had been photographed in a dark room, and the
teeth *had* been luminous, as had been the tip of the ap-
pendage growing out from between the eyes.

Less frightening and more impressive in many respects
was *Gigantura* (Fig. 23) which was labeled as a large rep-

FIG. 23. *Gigantura*, fish with telescope eyes.

resentative of the fish fauna of the deep sea. Its eel-like body
was 4¼ inches long and it had been taken from a depth of
8250 feet. The whole body was the most beautiful mother-of-
pearl color on a pink background; the long trailing tail (six
inches of it) looked like silver threads. And the eyes were
of a shape that had never been seen before; they were like
built-in opera glasses. The scientific designation, logically, was
"telescope eyes."

Nor were these telescope eyes just an accomplishment of
the fishes. Octopi had them too. There was a 4-inch octopus

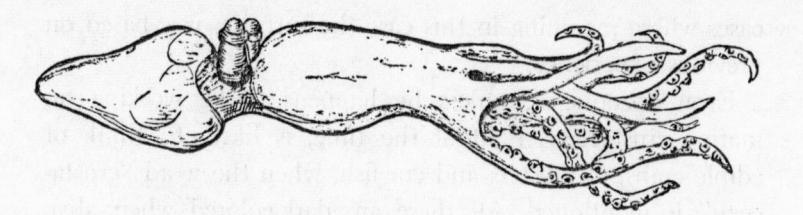

FIG. 24. *Amphitretus*, octopus with telescope eyes.

called *Amphitretus* which also had telescope eyes (Fig. 24). It was colorless and looked somewhat translucent. I can't tell whether this was its natural appearance or whether being preserved in alcohol had robbed it of what color it originally had. By the time I saw it, it had been in alcohol for some sixteen years and that, unfortunately, does cause bleaching.

The men of the *Valdivia* seem to have been generally somewhat more lucky than the men of the *Challenger* because they quite often could still have a quick look at the living deep-sea animals. True, the creatures died soon thereafter, but they were still seen alive. It must have been a difference of faster winches and general technical improvement in the catching equipment.

At any event, the men expressed their surprise at how colorful deep-sea life turned out to be. They probably had reasoned consciously that color did not matter in a permanently dark environment, and then had drawn the subconscious conclusion that the denizens of the extreme deep would therefore be black. Well, the conclusion had been wrong; the reasoning should have stopped with the statement that color does not matter in a permanently dark environment. So the animals had color, only it did not matter.

The fishes were mother-of-pearl color, or pink, or dark blue and *sometimes* black. The crabs, to everybody's surprise, were usually pink or red. This again was one of the

cases where reasoning in this case the surprise, was based on previous experience.

Even a zoologist, unless he happens to be working on marine crustaceans right at the time, is likely to think of edible crabs, of lobsters and crayfish, when the word "crustacean" is mentioned. All these are dark-colored when alive and it is just the fact that they have turned red that announces that they are ready to eat.

If you ask a zoologist why, he will readily explain that the color of the living lobster or crayfish is due to two pigments in the shell. One is blue, the other red. It so happens that the blue pigment is destroyed by heat (it does not dissolve in the cooking water, as you can sometimes read; if it did, the water would turn blue) so that only the heat-resistant red pigment is left. Hence the boiled crayfish and the broiled lobster are red.

After finishing this explanation, the same zoologist will even point out that one can occasionally find crayfish in which one or both pigments are missing. If both are missing, the crayfish looks dirty white, of course. If the red pigment is missing, it looks a rather beautiful light steel blue, and if the blue pigment is missing, the crayfish is pinkish red.

Well, yes, that is what the man *knows*. The occasional reddish living crayfish is an unusual case. So, when he sees a netful of red crabs and prawns break the surface of the ocean, he is still surprised because they are all red. He did not expect them to have the red pigment only. But they do.

It must be said that the zoologist, if he could spend some time at the bottom of the ocean, would not get used to red crabs and prawns either. If he were at the bottom of the Indian Ocean, where it is about 3500 feet deep, and sat perfectly still; he might see a red deep-sea prawn (*Nematocarcinus*) approach him. The picture would be something

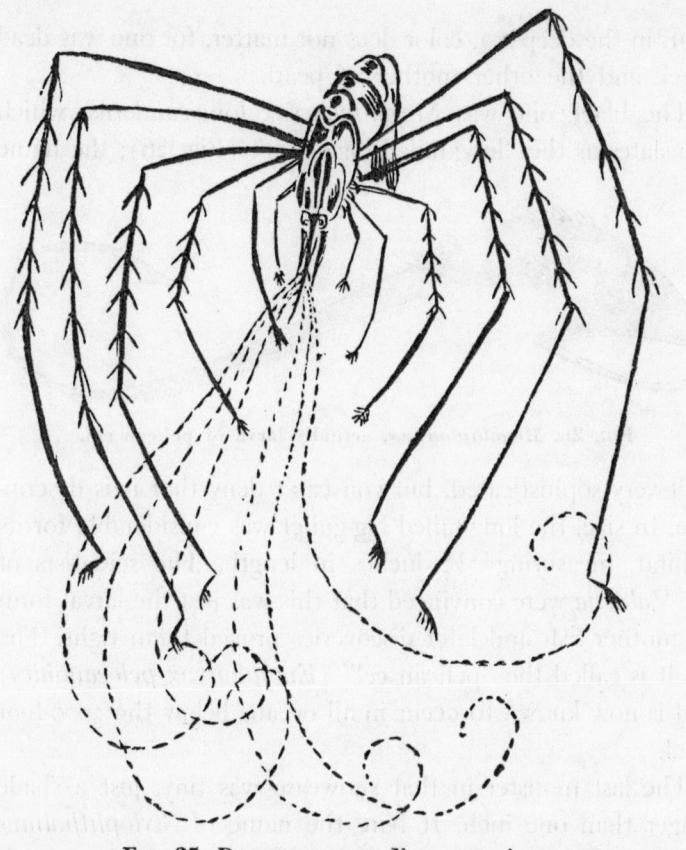

FIG. 25. Deep-sea prawn *Nematocarcinus.*

like Fig. 25. These crustaceans eject a luminous liquid, presumably to blind their enemies when attacked, and it is reported that this liquid clings to their own bodies for a while. But in the light beam of a lamp, the crab would look red.

However, this discussion has taken me away from the showcase at the Natural History Museum in Berlin where I spent much time in wonder when I was about twelve. There were two especially weird things in it. Again they proved

that, in the deep sea, color does not matter, for one was dead black and the other mother of pearl.

The black one was *Megalopharynx longicaudatus*, which translates as the "long-tailed big-gullet" (Fig. 26); the name

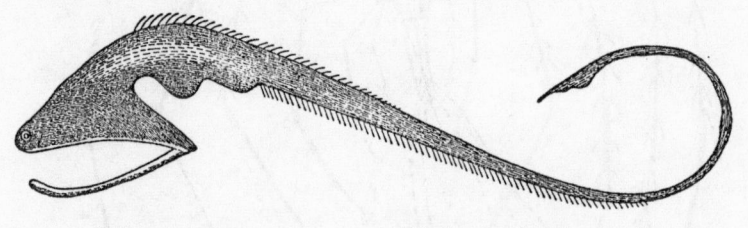

FIG. 26. *Megalopharynx*, actually larva of pelican eel.

isn't very sophisticated, but you can't deny that it is descriptive. In size, the long-tailed big-gullet was considerable for its habitat, measuring 7½ inches in length. The scientists of the *Valdivia* were convinced that this was just the larval form of another fish and later discoveries proved them right. The adult is called the "pelican eel" (*Eurypharynx pelecanoides*) and is now known to occur in all oceans below the 3000-foot level.

The last monster in that showcase was tiny, just a shade longer than one inch. It bore the name of *Stylophthalmus Braueri* and had been caught in the Indian Ocean at a depth of 6600 feet (Fig. 27). It also was a larval form. Why its eyes are on such long stalks is not known; larval forms do not always make sense even though one wishes they would.

It has just been mentioned that the pelican eel occurs in all oceans. Successive expeditions have tended to show that the fauna of the deep sea seems to be rather uniform, which, since the environment is rather uniform, is not really surprising. A fish caught in one ocean by one expedition at 4500 feet was caught by another expedition at 5000 feet in another ocean and by a third expedition at 3500 feet in still

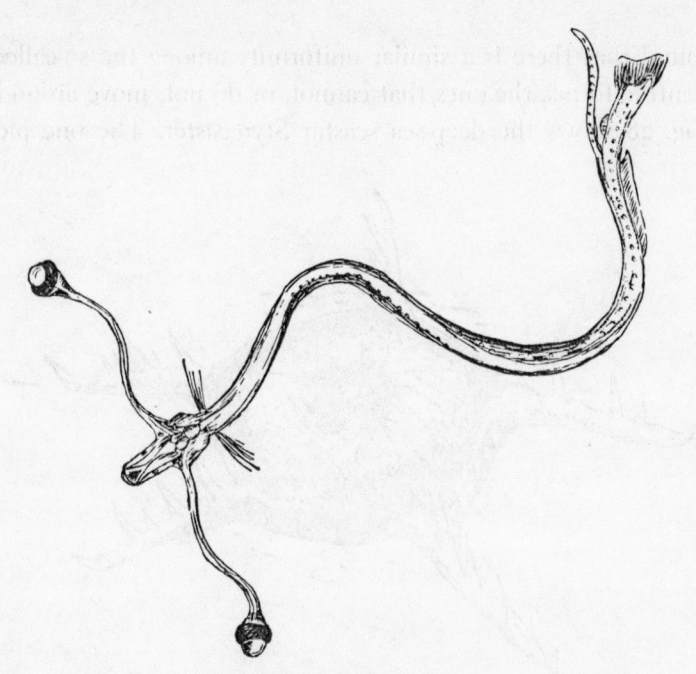

FIG. 27. *Stylophthalmus*, another deep-sea fish larva.

another ocean. The V*aldivia* itself provided different examples.

Nor is this uniformity restricted to what the German scientist called, in self-defense, the bathypelagic fishes. As has been explained earlier, the term "pelagic" means anything that swims or drifts around far from the shore; the deep-sea zoologists had to subdivide the term once more into "epipelagic" and "bathypelagic." Life forms found within the first 500 feet of depth, measuring from the ocean's surface, are called epipelagic, the ones in water deeper than 500 feet are the bathypelagic forms.

That the bathypelagic fauna of the oceans is rather uniform is not too surprising since conditions below 500 feet are alike practically everywhere. But the V*aldivia* expedition

found that there is a similar uniformity among the so-called benthic forms, the ones that cannot, or do not, move around. Fig. 28 shows the deep-sea seastar *Styracaster*. The one pic-

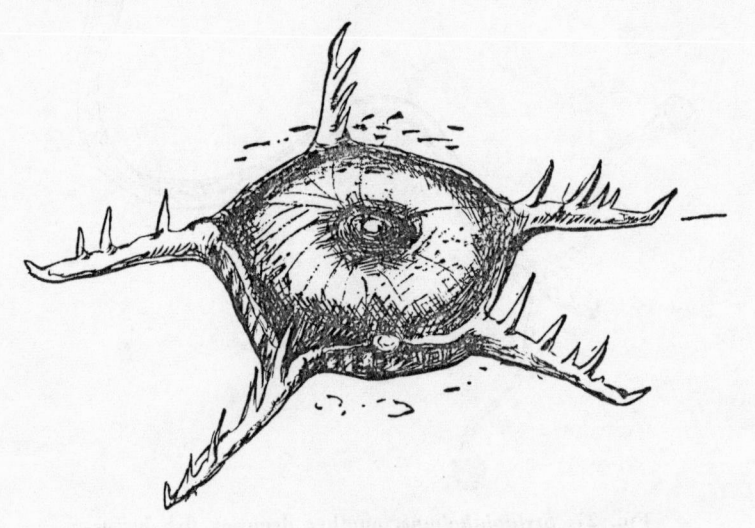

FIG. 28. *Styracaster*, abyssal seastar of wide distribution.

tured here was 2¾ inches across and was dredged up from the Atlantic from about 8000 feet. Another one just like it, but 6 inches across, was dredged from 17,000 feet in the Indian Ocean. Other crinoids (the *Valdivia* discovered several new species) also were the same in widely separated areas. The same went for sponges.

There are, it should be explained, three main types of sponges. The best known of them, the bath sponge, is a representative of the "Horny Sponges." Its structure consists of spongin fibers. The second group are the calcareous sponges, and the third the glass sponges with a silica skeleton. The glass sponges are often very beautiful and have shapes that remind the observer of artifacts—many look like intricate vases or bottles.

Some of these glass sponges which had come on the market via Japan had actually been thought to be artificial and had been much admired as the product of Japanese glass blowers. To the best of my knowledge, the Japanese never had any special reputation as glass blowers, nor do I know where the Japanese got them. The *Valdivia* found these types, which had been thought artificial, in many places, always deep down, always alike, no matter how far apart they grew.

Naturally the *Valdivia* expedition was not the last of its kind. It was followed one year later by the Dutch *Siboga* expedition under Professor Max Weber. Then followed a Norwegian deep-sea expedition on a vessel which was named —what else?—the *Michael Sars*. There were American expeditions (*Albatross*), Danish expeditions on the ships *Dana I* and *Dana II* (these paid special attention to the life history of the common eel, still completely unknown as late as 1912), and finally the Danish *Galathea* expedition.

In the meantime, the problem was attacked from an entirely different angle. Most of what the *Valdivia* had found was, by definition, benthic. It was either grown to the bottom, like those glass sponges, or else it was not likely to move far, like the seastars and even most of the fishes. Just how much bathypelagic life there actually was remained to be investigated, and the best way of doing it was to put a man in a position where he could observe it directly. I am, of course, speaking of William Beebe's bathysphere.

William Beebe and his assistants were the first men to actually see bathypelagic fishes in their natural habitat and they were surprised at how much of it there was. All I can do is to urge you to read William Beebe's *Half Mile Down* which was reprinted in 1951 and is still available.

Since I am recommending books, I'll go on and recommend equally strongly that you spend two or three hours

with *The Galathea Deep Sea Expedition* (published by the Macmillan Company) which produced results every bit as interesting as those of the *Challenger* and the *Valdivia*.

The *Galathea* expedition (it took place during the years 1950–52) confirmed the earlier impression that the bathypelagic fauna was of worldwide distribution. The fish *Bathymicrops* is an insignificant-looking small and blind fish, but

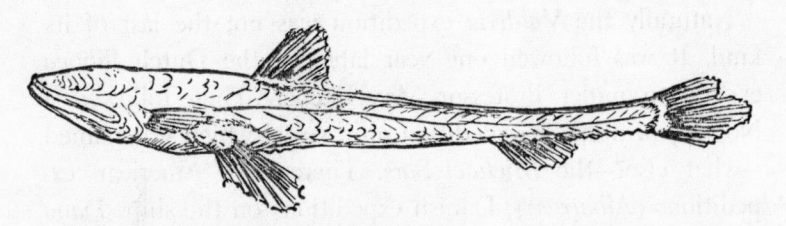

FIG. 29. Blind deep-sea fish *Bathymicrops*, of worldwide distribution.

it is widely distributed. It was caught in the North Atlantic 16,500 feet down by the *Michael Sars*, three times in the Atlantic by the *Albatross* (at 14,000 feet off Northwest Africa, at 18,000 feet in mid-Atlantic near the equator and at 17,000 feet near the North Coast of South America), and three times by the *Galathea* (at about 15,000 feet near the southern tip of Africa, at about 16,000 feet off the African East Coast near the equator, and at 19,300 feet just north of the North Island of New Zealand).

The route of the *Galathea* was similar to that of the *Valdivia*: from Copenhagen through the English Channel, down the West Coast of Africa, up the East Coast to the Seychelles Islands, across the Indian Ocean to Ceylon, then through the Sunda Sea to Australia, around New Zealand, up to Hawaii, then to San Francisco, from there to the Panama Canal and, cutting across the Atlantic, back to Copenhagen.

The *Galathea* secured a number of specimens of the invertebrate life of the abyssal regions which do not seem to belong to Earth. A deep-sea cucumber (*Scotoplanes*) measuring about 3¾ inches in length was found off the Philippines at 22,000 and at 33,000 feet. Probably it spends its life buried in the mud (Fig. 30).

FIG. 30. A deep-sea holothurian, *Scotoplanes*, probably an inactive type.

An even more unusual-looking holothurian (sea cucumber, that is) was taken from about 18,000 feet from the bottom between the northern end of Madagascar and the African mainland. Eight specimens of *Psychropotes* (Fig. 31) were

FIG. 31. Deep-sea holothurian, *Psychropotes*, probably a very active type.

taken in one haul, the largest being a foot in length, the smallest eight inches. They probably plow through the ooze, hunting worms.

Fig. 32 shows a rather large crustacean (one of the so-

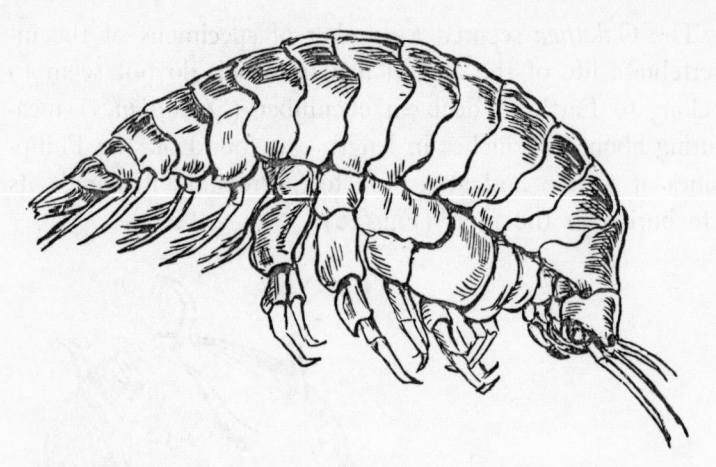

FIG. 32. Deep-sea crustacean, *Eurythenes gryllus*, probably active type too.

called amphipods) taken by the *Galathea* in the Indian Ocean from depths up to 16,000 feet. This crustacean seems to be swimming some distance above the bottom as well as moving around on the bottom. It grows to a length of about four inches.

Now, an even dozen expeditions after Michael Sars' first probing of the deep sea, we can make a few generalizations.

To begin with, no place in the deep sea, which, after all, covers about 60 per cent of the Earth's surface, is completely lifeless. In general, it seems that the life-forms are smaller the deeper you go, but some surprises in that respect are easily possible. So far, the areas which the *Challenger* men entered as "red ooze" on their charts seem to have the smallest number of inhabitants per square mile. The fauna of the deepest deep sea seems to be essentially benthic; apparently food is so scarce that obtaining it is largely accidental, so that it makes little difference whether the organism moves around actively searching for food or just lies in wait.

The absolutely sessile forms are too far down in the scale of evolution to have developed luminous organs, especially since a number of them, the sponges, are eyeless under any circumstances.

Crustaceans can, as has been mentioned, eject a luminous liquid. Luminous organs have been found, to the best of my knowledge, only on fishes and on octopi. In both cases, the animal seems to be able to control these organs, to be able to switch them on or off. Crustaceans and fishes, as well as octopi, have gone to both extremes as regards eyes. They either are completely blind or they have developed the largest eyes for their body size known to naturalists.

It appears that none of the forms inhabiting the deep sea originated there. They, or rather their ancestors, all seem to have migrated from higher layers.

The research work was determined at the beginning by the desire to find out how far life extended into the depth. It was only natural to investigate the sea bottom first, after it had been learned that there was something to investigate. The deep sea which is *not* near the bottom has been somewhat neglected by comparison. But we already know that it is richer in life than the bottom itself.

One is naturally tempted, at this point in history, to compare the deep sea to space. The comparison is easy. In both cases, we know it is there. In both cases, we know it is immense in extent. In both cases, we know there is something to investigate.

And, in both cases, we have to start any discussion with the words: "We have only just begun."

CHAPTER IX

FORERUNNERS OF THE PLANETARIUM

"THE FORERUNNER of the planetarium of today is the orrery, and the forerunner of the orrery . . ."

When I said this sentence aloud at home, both my daughters interrupted me in unison—a unison that would normally need half a dozen rehearsals to make it as perfect as it was. But they did not say the same thing. One of them said: "The what?" while the other, not trusting my pronunciation, said: "Spell it." I did spell it. But that did not clarify the situation at all; they swore they had never heard the word.

I pointed out that both of them had repeatedly seen a very fine orrery. The answer again came in unison: "Where?"

I'll explain what an orrery is in a moment, but it seems to me that the word should be explained first. If somebody had asked me, say about a year ago, about the derivation of the word I probably would have guessed that it was somehow derived from the Latin *hora*, meaning *"hour"*—assuming that somebody in England, a century or two ago, had dropped the initial "h" somewhere along the way.

My guess would have been ingenious and totally wrong. It so happens that the word orrery is not a corruption of a Latin term; it is a name. The device is named after Charles Boyle, Fourth Earl of Orrery. And the earl was not even the inventor; he merely had a very fine one in his castle circa 1725.

After getting the word out of the way I can proceed to the
explanation of what an orrery really is.

It is a model of the solar system and there is a very fine
one at the Hayden Planetarium in New York City, where it
is called the Copernican Room. The planets, represented by
spheres of the proper size, hang from the ceiling and move
in circular tracks, accompanied by their moons which move
around them. Of course the motion has been speeded up, or
else one would not be able to see it. A similar large orrery
is at the Morehead Planetarium, Chapel Hill, N.C., while
a third one can be found in the German Museum in Munich.

In all three cases a modern planetarium is housed in the
same building, so that visitors can see easily how they differ
in function. The orrery shows how the planets move in their
orbits and the mechanism could, if desired, be stopped at the
moment where the positions of the model planets agree
with the positions of the actual planets on that day. That
is how the solar system would appear at that moment, as
seen from the outside. The modern planetarium, on the
other hand, produces the view from the earth. In fact, the
starry sky of the planetarium is superior to the actual night
sky in several respects. In the first place, it does not matter
what the weather is doing outside the dome. In the second
place, the motions can be speeded up so that you can actually follow the motions of Mars among the fixed stars.
Finally, you are not restricted geographically to the place
where you happen to be.

Nor are you limited to the time in which you happen to
live. The planetarium can reproduce the sky as it looked
from Ur of the Chaldees in 1950 B.C. when Alpha Draconis
was the pole star; or it can reproduce the sky as seen from
Manhattan Island in about 12,000 A.D. when Vega will be

the North Star and the Southern Cross will be above the horizon over New York Bay.

While the orreries in Munich, New York and Chapel Hill—listing them in chronological order of their completion—are large and expensive and therefore rare devices, smaller orreries exist in many places. The smallest and simplest device which could still be called an orrery is one that consists of an electric light bulb with a reflector in the middle, a small globe of the earth and a small sphere representing the moon. When you turn a crank the moon will start spinning around the earth and the earth will start turning and describe its orbit around the sun. It is a teaching device for demonstrating the phases of the moon and for showing why the moon is not eclipsed by the earth's shadow each time it goes around the earth.

There can be no doubt that a large number of orreries which once existed have never been described in print. Those we know about all date from 1700 or later and are, therefore, models of the solar system after Copernicus and Kepler had been generally accepted. Whether, say prior to 1500, anybody ever tried to build an orrery according to Ptolemy, with the earth in the center, is not known. It probably was not done because at the time the armillary sphere (we'll get to that soon) was considered sufficient for the purpose of explaining the construction of the universe.

But we cannot be certain because the written word is incomplete in a very peculiar way. Writers, especially at a time when there were very few of them, wrote selectively. They either wrote down what happened to have made an impression, or else they wrote what they thought the future might wish to know. The result of this attitude is that we have very little knowledge of those things which these writers took for granted. If we now know what kinds of knives and forks were

FIG. 33. Tycho Brahe's great armilla, mounted in his second observatory of Stjerneborg on the island of Hveen. (From his own work on his instruments.)

used at a baronial banquet in, say, 1600, we are likely to know this because of actual knives and forks that have somehow come down to our time, not from contemporary descriptions. Let me add one more example. We would know from contemporary chronicles, bills of sale and similar things that the gold coin of the reign of Henry VII, minted around 1495, was called an "angel." But it would be a major literary research project (and one that is likely to fail) to find out how an "angel" looked. Of course nobody needs to undertake this research project since we have the actual coin; it isn't even a great rarity.

The fact that a pre-Copernician orrery is not mentioned anywhere is therefore no proof that none ever existed. It merely proves that it, if it existed, did not become famous enough to be described. But let us assume that none was built. And that brings us to the question of what preceded the orrery.

Here you get two opinions, depending on point of view. Those who consider an orrery mainly a complicated mechanical device are likely to name the astronomical clocks, which were the pride of many a European city between 1400 and 1600. Astronomers, however, will be inclined to name the armillary sphere as the forerunner, since it was an attempt at representing the universe.

And the armillary sphere, or armilla—both terms are used almost interchangeably, though a more complicated example is usually called an armillary sphere—in turn goes back to the celestial globes of antiquity.

Celestial globes were just what their name means, globes on which the positions of the major stars and constellations were engraved on the outside. An especially fine example is a celestial globe with a diameter of not quite 26 inches, supported by a statue of Atlas. The sculpture, of Greek origin,

dates back to about 300 B.C. and is now in the National Museum at Naples. A number of other celestial globes, usually made of bronze or silver, has been mentioned by Muslim writers, especially if they were made for the ruling Caliph, but the oldest still extant example is one made in 1080 A.D. But as a device for teaching the solid sphere had a drawback. It showed the stars on the outside of a globe. The pupil had to imagine, if he could, that he saw the stars from the inside.

The armillary sphere was a skeleton sphere; you could look through it. There is a mural dating back to about 50 B.C. on the wall of a villa at Boscoreale, not far from Pompeii, which shows a sphere consisting only of the imaginary circles, like equator, arctic and antarctic circles, and the ecliptic. It is not known, of course, whether this mural was just a painting or whether it can be taken as an illustration of this kind which actually existed then. If it does depict something then in actual existence, the model for the painting would be a very early armillary sphere. If it is a painting showing a principle, then it was the forerunner of actual spheres to be built.

The early pictures of armillary spheres which definitely are illustrations depicting existing spheres can be found in manuscripts of the thirteenth and fourteenth centuries. They show the equator, the tropics, the polar circles, the ecliptic and usually a number of meridians. After that, as we know from actual examples that have been preserved, the craftsmen took over and lavished their skill on the job of building a "good" sphere. The ecliptic was no longer a wire ring in the proper position. It became a band of chased copper with the signs of the zodiac engraved upon it. There were movable pointers for the more important stars. In some the planets were added and could be moved along wire loops by hand. But Venus was not just a ball of ivory, or Mars a ball of copper—they were symbolical figures representing Venus and Mars. It is no

exaggeration to say that some of these spheres were smothered in elaboration.

I have often been asked by people who looked at one of these elaborate armillary spheres (or just photographs of them) how they were used for astronomical observations. The answer is that they weren't. They were teaching devices for classroom use. The teacher might, for example, move the figure representing the sun into the constellation Virgo. He would then explain that, with this position of the sun, the sign of Virgo and the neighboring constellations would be in the daylight sky and hence invisible, but that the constellations of the zodiac opposite the position of the sun—"look through the sphere and you'll see them"—would be in the night sky.

I know of a modern astronomer who uses an armillary sphere for the purpose of teaching his students how astronomy was taught in the past. It not only does this particular job, it also proves that the armillary sphere itself was a rather good teaching device for memorizing and understanding the apparent motions of the celestial bodies.

Of course the armillary sphere was built with the assumption that the earth was in the center of the universe. The more elaborate specimens do have a globe of the earth in the center. This enhances the sphere as a model of what the world was believed to be, but the central globe interfered with the teaching so that the spheres actually used had an empty center so that you could look through the sphere.

While the armillary sphere was meant for students, the astronomical clocks were meant for the public. A typical arrangement (much simplified) is shown in Fig. 34. The upper clock was simply a clock, while the lower face showed the zodiac. There two arrangements were possible and both were used. Either you had the zodiac immobile, just painted on

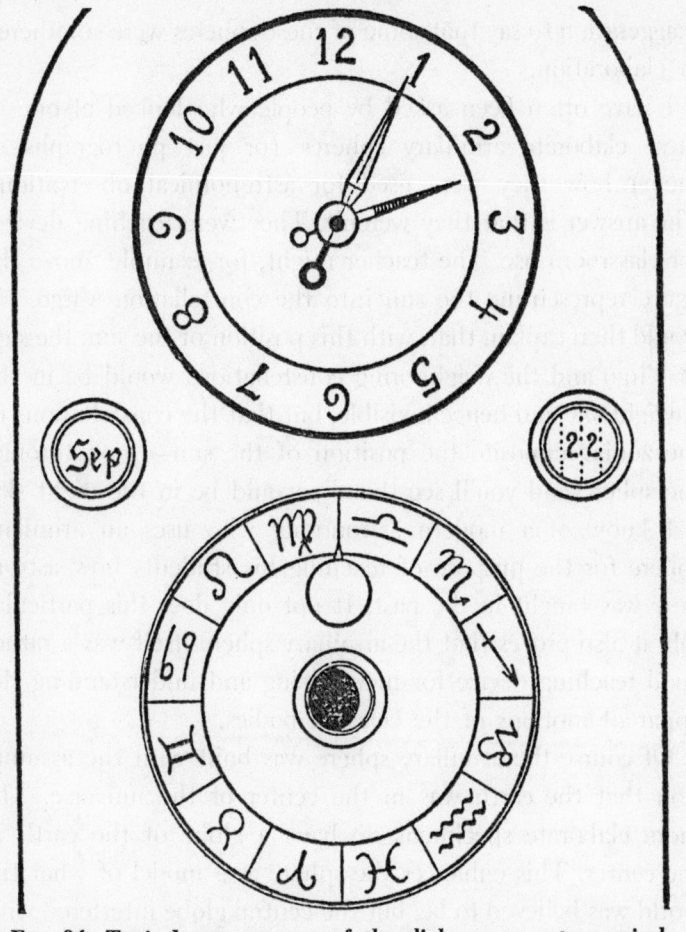

FIG. 34. Typical arrangement of the dials on an astronomical clock of the sixteenth century.

the background in gold, silver, green, blue, red and a few other colors and you had a golden disk representing the sun at the end of a pointer, moving it over the signs of the zodiac once a year. Or else (as assumed for Fig. 34) you had the golden disk of the sun immobile and the zodiac painted on a slowly moving circle. Separate dials gave the month and the

date, while a slowly turning sphere which was half silver and half black showed the phases of the moon.

A look at such a clock therefore provided the date, the time of day, the prevailing lunar phase and the position of the sun along the zodiac.

But this was only the actual information supplied by such a clock. There was still room for elaboration. The astronomical clock built in Strassbourg in 1352 was an example. We know that the master who built this cathedral clock spent two full years on this work.[1] A quick description will show why. A rooster, perched on top, crowed every hour. Then a statue of the Virgin Mary appeared and the three Wise Men passed in front of her, bowing. The crowing of the rooster was followed by a hymn on a carillon. And there was a somewhat stylized human figure with a pointer moving over it, indicating that part of the body which was astrologically favored for bleeding if bleeding was deemed necessary.

Yes, it was possible to be more elaborate than that, as was proved in 1530 by Kaspar Brunner, when the City of Bern requested him to build an astronomical clock for a tower especially built for the purpose. The clock part consisted of the customary two dials, one giving the hours and minutes, the other the astronomical information for astrological purposes. Since Bern was in a republic, and since the clock was not a church clock but a city clock, Brunner could not use kings and princes as had been done elsewhere, nor could he use a religious theme for elaboration. Hence the famous clock of Bern marked the hours as follows:

Five minutes before the hour a rooster crowed and the figure of a fool sitting above him hit two different bells. After that a royal figure, representing the sun, turned its hand

---

[1] Legend says that his name was Jehan Boerhave and that he was the pupil of Arab craftsmen, but in fact, the name of the master is unknown.

FIG. 35. Picture of an armilla with zodiac from a book by the Austrian astronomer George von Peuerbach (died 1461) printed in 1515. The lady to the left is labeled "Astrology" the man to the right is Ptolemy.

holding an hourglass and a bear (the coat of arms of the city features a bear) who sat opposite the rooster shook his head. Thereupon, on a lower gallery, a whole troop of bears pranced across, some walking, some on horseback. After they were gone, the rooster crowed again, then a very tall figure of a man, dressed all in black, appeared, raised a hand holding a hammer and struck a square bell. The new hour had started . . .

Let's get back to representations of the sky.

The earliest known example is a tent made by an unknown Arab craftsman. It was conquered during the Fifth Crusade; when Emperor Friedrich II of Hohenstaufen returned to Italy in 1229 he brought it with him. It is described as having had a cupola-shaped roof showing the constellations. A hidden clockwork made the stars move, as the not very detailed description says; in all probability it turned the whole cupola so that a man sitting inside the tent could watch the motion of the stars across the night sky in accelerated time.

Unfortunately this earliest forerunner of the planetarium is lost without a trace. No good description is known. No drawing, if one was made, is still in existence.

The next attempt to represent the appearance of the starry sky is much better documented. It is known as Gottorp's Globus, named after Duke Friedrich von Holstein-Gottorp, who had it built for him. Scientific advisor was the mathematician and astronomer, Adam Olearius; the man who did the actual building was Andreas Busch. The work took from 1656 to 1664.

It was a sphere of sheet copper, with a diameter of 11½ feet. On the outside it was painted to show the continents and oceans of the earth. But all the more important stars were represented by holes drilled through the copper so that

Duke Friedrich, when he entered his globe during daylight hours, had a representation of the night sky. Since the ducal family had a Russian branch, the famous globe was taken to St. Petersburg in 1713; I have not been able to find out what has happened to it since.

The Gottorp globe found a successor in London in 1851 when James Wyld, M.P., had a sixty-foot globe built in the center of Leicester Square. Mr. Wyld's original idea had been to show the extent of the British Empire to Londoners and visitors by means of a very large globe. But he then realized that a person standing near a very large globe can see only a small portion of that globe and he found a solution in an inverted globe.

The continents and oceans and rivers and so forth were put on the inside of his sixty-foot sphere in bas relief. That way a visitor could look at a much larger area at a glance and, if the reporter of the *Illustrated London News* of the time can be trusted, the globe was large enough so that a visitor would not realize that he looked at a concave surface. But James Wyld's inverted globe—called the "georama" in some references—had nothing to do with astronomy or a representation of the sky.

It seems a long way from Gottorp's globe to the modern planetarium, but the long way was traversed in a single step, without any intermediary developments. The way this came about was as follows: In 1903, Dr. Oskar von Miller, the son of Ferdinand von Miller, who was the director of the Royal Foundry in Munich, outlined his ideas for a museum which was to be devoted to accomplishments in science and technology. The museum conceived by Dr. von Miller now exists; it is the German Museum in Munich.

Part of the museum was to be devoted to astronomy, which meant a "planetarium." When von Miller used this word he

meant a large orrery. But in addition to a large orrery von Miller also wanted something that represented the sky as seen in a clear night. Knowing about Gottorp's globe, he had something like the movable cupola of an astronomical observatory in mind, with holes for the stars so that the night sky could be seen during the day by way of daylight shining through the holes. If operation during the night should be scheduled, floodlights could do the job.

While Dr. von Miller had a general idea of how it could be done, he knew very well that he would need specialists for the details. He sent a request to the firm of Carl Zeiss in Jena, which did not only build optical instruments, but observatory cupolas as well. At the Zeiss office they started to think. Wouldn't it be better to use light bulbs of different strengths for the stars? That would make the operation of the new planetarium completely independent of the weather. But what about the planets?

Dr. von Miller had not prescribed any figures but he wanted his planetarium large enough to accommodate up to a hundred visitors at a time. This meant that the planets would have to be illuminated balls at the ends of pointers that would have to be as much as twenty or more feet in length. The designing engineers groaned at the thought. But the task was, after all, only difficult. Nobody had asked for anything impossible and they had all the leeway they wanted when it came to detail. So they went to work.

Before anything could be shown the first World War began and everything was delayed for four years. But there had been enough preliminary work so that a first model was ready some eight months or so after the end of that war. Then it turned out that the first idea of how to do it had quite a number of drawbacks.

The "planets" could not be made visible by means of spot-

lights without illuminating part of the dome. And the big cupola which carried all the light bulbs representing the stars could not be turned, except so noisily that the lecturer's voice would be drowned out.

After this experience the director of the Zeiss works, Dr. Walter Bauersfeld, came to the conclusion that the planets should be projected against the dome. But if you project the planets, why not the fixed stars as well? Therefore he proposed that the dome should not rotate but be solid and motionless, serving only as the projection surface for the images originating from a series of small projectors located in the center of the sphere, that is to say in the center of the floor of the seating area.

The suggestion was accepted, but it took five years until all the minor difficulties could be overcome.

The first planetarium—as we now understand the term—was opened in Munich in the late summer of 1924. The Zeiss projector did not yet have the now familiar shape resembling a monstrous dumbbell. There was one projector for the fixed stars and an inclined cylinder for everything else. But it worked, and the firm of Carl Zeiss quickly received requests from other cities. The second Zeiss planetarium was built in Düsseldorf, the next one in Nuremberg and, after some delay, one in Berlin. In the meantime American museums and scientific institutions had negotiated with Zeiss too, and the first planetarium in the United States was the Adler Planetarium in Chicago. It opened its doors on May 10, 1930. The Fels Planetarium in Philadelphia was the second (November 1, 1933), the Griffith Observatory and Planetarium in Los Angeles the third (May 14, 1935). New York's Hayden Planetarium followed hard on the heels of the Griffith Planetarium; it was opened on October 2, 1935. The Buhl Planetarium in Pittsburgh was the fifth (October 24, 1939) and the

Morehead Planetarium of the University of North Carolina in Chapel Hill, N.C., rounded out the first half dozen when it was opened on May 10, 1949.

How many are in operation in the United States now?

According to a letter which Armand N. Spitz wrote to me on July 23, 1964, the number is "between 300 and 400"—and I might add that Armand N. Spitz is mainly responsible for this large number.

The fully developed Zeiss projector was a modern miracle, but modern miracles tend to be expensive. The Zeiss projector was no exception. Spitz wanted a projector that would do what the Zeiss instrument could do, or at least come close, but that would be within financial reach of High Schools, smaller museums and libraries in smaller communities.

In 1947 he succeeded in building a small and relatively inexpensive functioning projector.

The projector for the fixed stars consisted of a dodecahedron made of black plastic sheets. Inside the dodecahedron was a light bulb. The stars were holes of different sizes drilled into the black plastic through which the light of the bulb shone. To produce the diurnal motion of the stars the machine was rotated around an axis parallel to the axis of the earth. Changes in latitude were produced by tilting this axis. The planets and the sun and moon were handled by separate projectors. One of the first Spitz projectors was installed at the U. S. Merchant Marine Academy at Kings Point, N.Y. Within ten years of its creation, nearly 200 of the small projectors were installed all over the United States.

But while this was going on, the Spitz projector grew, too. Model B, as it was called, was a much bigger projector, resembling in external shape the later model of the Zeiss projector. But while the Zeiss projector has a solid mounting, the Model B projector was suspended from cables, so that it

seemed to float in air during a demonstration. The first of the Model B projectors was installed at the *Centro Municipal de Divulgacion Cientifica* in Montevideo, Uruguay. The second went to Flint College in Flint, Mich., and the third to the U. S. Air Force Academy in Colorado Springs, Colorado.

The advent of the space age added a new request. Up to 1957 everybody had been quite happy to overcome time and geographical location on the ground by means of a planetarium projector. But then the question came up how things would look when seen from space.

The first projection device which is not earthbound, though it rests on a solid mounting like the Zeiss instruments, is the one at Abrams Planetarium of Michigan State University in East Lansing, Michigan. It has the somewhat cumbersome name of Intermediate Space Transit Planetarium or ISTP. The Spitz ISTP can go into a satellite orbit around the earth, fly from the earth to the moon, make a loop around the moon and take up a parking orbit around the moon—or, at least it will look that way to the audience.

The next type—still under development—is the Space Transit Simulator of STS, which will be able to do what the ISTP does, but in addition to that it will be capable of flying to Mars and to Venus.

Astronauts getting ready for missions to Mars and to Venus will be able to use it for training. And the day is not too far off when an astronaut, after having returned from an interplanetary mission and being tired of answering questions of what things look like in space, will take his questioners by the hand, lead them to the nearest institution which owns an STS and say:

"Sit still now and see for yourself."

CHAPTER X

THE NEARLY ALWAYS USEFUL "BEAN CURVE"

SIR FRANCIS GALTON, who died in 1911 just one month before
reaching the age of eighty-nine, was one of the important
scientists of the latter part of the nineteenth century, even
though his name is not very well known anymore.

He was born in Birmingham in 1822. By the time little
Francis received his first lessons, one of his cousins who was
thirteen years older studied for the ministry and passed his
spare time as an enthusiastic collector of English beetles. The
name of the beetle-collecting cousin was Charles Darwin; the
grandfather of them both was Dr. Erasmus Darwin. By the
time Charles Darwin went on a voyage around the world on
the H.M.S. *Beagle*, instead of mounting the pulpit, Francis
Galton was at Trinity College, Cambridge studying anthro-
pology. At the age of twenty-three he went traveling too, first
to the Sudan, then to South-West Africa. After his return he
first wrote about his travels and then turned to the study of
meteorology. His *Meteorographica* (1863) was one of the first
comprehensive books on the then new science of weather research.

That he did not stick to meteorology but changed course
once more was the fault of his cousin.

Charles Darwin's *Origin of Species* had been published in
1859. Galton read it, of course, and realized that here was a
whole collection of new fields and that Darwin, thorough as

he had been, had not been able to cover everything. Therefore he began to work in a few of these peripheral fields.

He became especially interested in heredity as applied to humans, and began statistical studies of hereditary traits. His studies involved the results of inheritance in certain families, but also of people who were not related but had something in common—for example genius, or color blindness, or a criminal record. The last subdivision led him to fingerprints, about which he wrote several books.

Heredity was understood in Galton's time, to the extent that it had been noticed that both parents passed on traits to their children, and that some traits were pronounced while others seemed to disappear. But it was also known that traits sometimes jumped across one generation. His own famous grandfather and famous grandson, Charles Darwin, were one example. The Mendelssohn family in Berlin was another one, where the middle member, the banker Abraham Mendelssohn, remarked that it was tough to be the son and the father of famous men. (His father had been the famous Jewish philosopher Moses Mendelssohn, his son was the composer Felix Mendelssohn-Bartholdy.) But the extremes, genius on the one side and idiocy on the other, were rare. The majority was in the middle.

One day Galton constructed, presumably for purposes of demonstration, a device which he called the Random Machine. (See Fig. 36.) It consisted of a funnel-like metal strip, mounted on a board. Below the funnel mouth were a large number of evenly distributed brads, and below them a number of vertical slots. The front of the whole was covered by a pane of glass. The top was open so that the experimenter could drop small steel balls into the funnel. The steel ball would roll down one of the slopes and then bounce its way

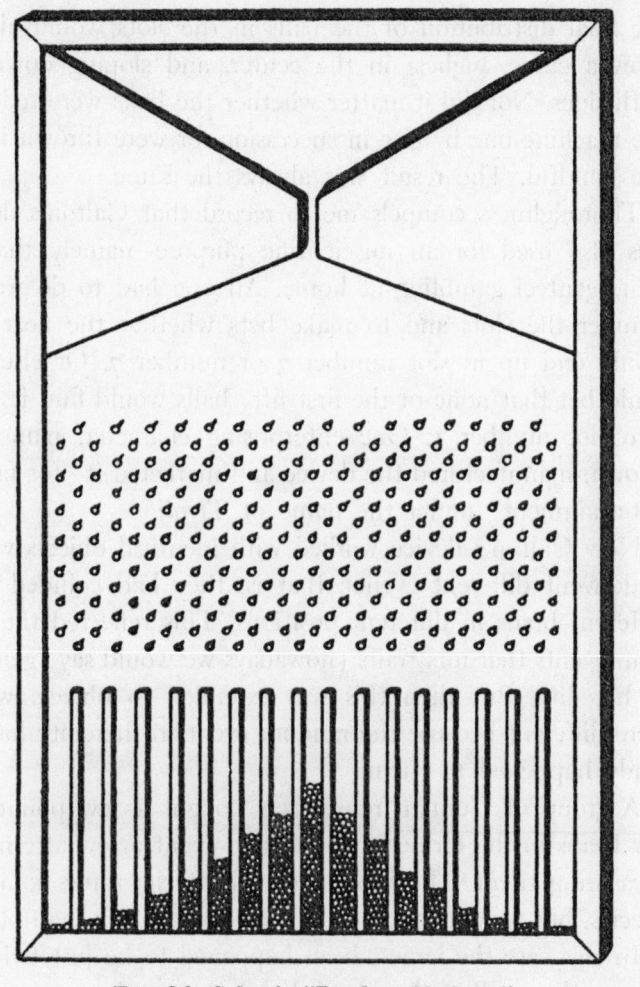

FIG. 36. Galton's "Random Machine."

through the row of brads. Finally it would end up in one of the slots.

It was impossible to tell in advance in which slot the ball would end up. But if a large number, at least a hundred, balls were used, the center slots would receive more of them, and

the final distribution of the balls in the slots would always show a curve, highest in the center, and sloping down on both sides. Nor did it matter whether the balls were fed into the machine one by one in succession, or were thrown in by the handful. The result was always the same.

Thoroughness compels me to record that Galton's device was also used for an unscientific purpose—namely that of some genteel gambling at home. All one had to do was to number the slots and to make bets whether the next ball would end up in slot number 3 or number 7. Or else one could bet that none of the first fifty balls would find its way into slot number 1. One enterprising character, name unknown, manufactured the device and marketed it "for family entertainment" under the name of *Tivoli*.

Now Galton's device worked with identical objects which underwent different events; that is, they had collided with different brads in different positions. This reflected the random events that mix traits (nowadays we would say "genes") in heredity. But then this was extended to objects which were different because the random events of heredity had already happened to them.

A group of German researchers bought a few pounds of dry beans in the farmer's market and spent a few afternoons measuring them. The beans were all of the same botanical species, but some of them were, of course, larger than others.

In this case the largest bean happened to be just twice as long as the smallest. A rack of chemical test tubes was pressed into service as a receiver. It was dubbed the "bean harp," since the row of vertical tubes reminded somebody with musical inclinations and some imagination of the strings of a harp. The largest bean went into test tube number 9, the smallest into test tube number 1; and the overall result of the sorting can be seen in Fig. 37. It was the same kind of curve.

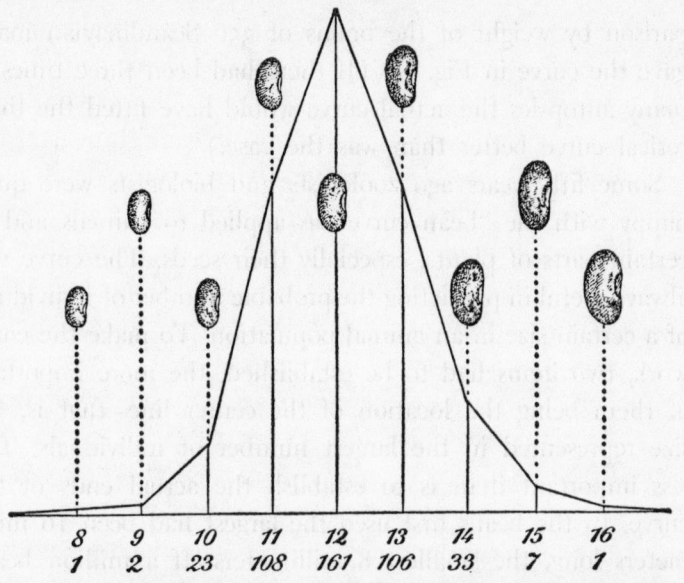

FIG. 37. The distribution of 442 beans picked at random. Upper line gives length in millimeters, lower line the number of beans.

The military, especially the Quartermaster Corps, became interested. If beans had such a definite curve showing the average numbers of beans of each size, that might apply to soldiers too—or rather to their uniforms and boots. Of course people differed far more from each other than did beans. Still it could do no harm to let a mathematician play around for some time with statistics of military inventories.

This, it may be necessary to note, was more than a decade before the outbreak of World War I. It may also be added that the mathematicians were disdainful of the biologists' term "bean curve" and at once talked about Gaussian curves.

In the meantime Swedish researchers had extended the bean curve to humans, or the most typically human part of them, namely the brain. In the course of autopsies made for all kinds of reasons the brain weights were noted. The com-

parison by weight of the brains of 350 Scandinavian males gave the curve in Fig. 38. (If there had been three times as many autopsies the actual curve would have fitted the theoretical curve better than was the case.)

Some fifty years ago zoologists and biologists were quite happy with the "bean curve" as applied to animals and to certain parts of plants, especially their seeds. The curve was always useful in predicting the probable number of individuals of a certain size in an animal population. To make the curve work, two items had to be established, the more important of them being the location of the center line—that is, the size represented in the largest number of individuals. The less important item is to establish the actual ends of the curve. In the beans first used the largest had been 16 millimeters long, the smallest 8 millimeters. If a million beans had been measured the largest might have been, say, 20 millimeters and the smallest 6 millimeters. But these would be

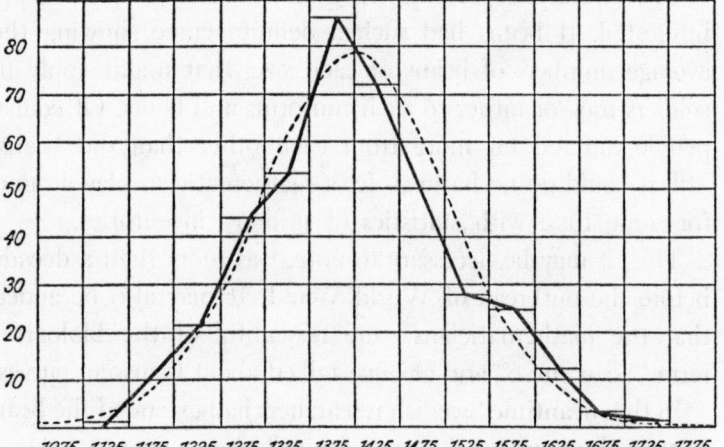

FIG. 38. Weight of the brain of 350 Scandinavian males. Vertical column at left gives number of individuals, horizontal column at bottom the weight in grams. Dotted line is the mathematical curve.

the practical limits. Even ten million beans would not yield one 200 millimeters (about 8 inches) long. They simply do not exist—even though the curve, written as an equation, might say that there should be one 200-millimeter bean in every ten or fifteen million.

Prior to World War I no practical conclusions were based on the bean curve, under whatever name. The reason probably was that private individuals still had their garments made to measure, while the military could set artificial limits and accept as draftees or volunteers only men of arbitrarily set minimum and maximum heights and sizes.

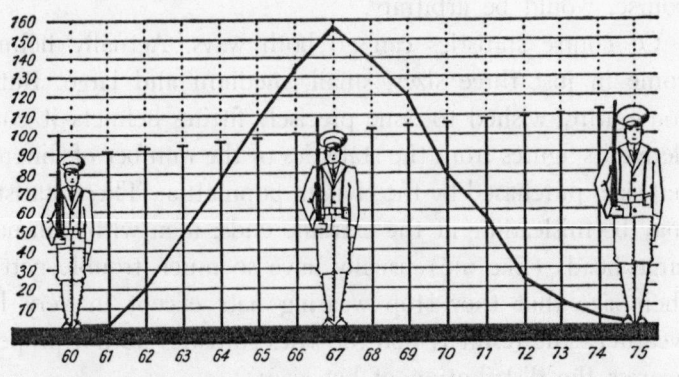

FIG. 39. Height of 1000 American soldiers, 1922. Vertical column at left is the number of individuals, horizontal figures at bottom give height in inches.

But after the first World War such studies, for the very practical purpose of military purchases of uniforms, underwear, socks and boots, were started. Fig. 39 shows the curve for 1000 American soldiers, a random group picked in 1922. The center line then was 5 feet 7 inches, represented by 157 men. One inch shorter was represented by 136 men and one inch taller by 138 men. The size range from 5 feet 5 inches to 5 feet 10 inches comprised 740 men—very nearly three-quarters of the 1000 soldiers fell into that size range.

It is easy to understand how a knowledge of these facts will influence decisions on military purchases.

Of course, this curve of the year 1922 no longer applies literally. People have grown since then and by now the center line may be 5 feet 8 inches instead of 5 feet 7 inches. Likewise the center line of the curve will vary with nationality. If I had actual statistics I would expect quite different center lines for the British army, the French army and the Japanese army.

But the curve itself would apply in every army, just with a different center line and different cutoff points—which, of course, would be arbitrary.

Of course statistics can go both ways. Actually helmets come in just three sizes, small, medium and large. But if some army wished to issue precisely fitting helmets it could derive its figures from the statistics of the number of different hat sizes purchased by the civilian population. These statistics may be misleading at the extreme ends; men with unusually large heads (like me) usually have so much trouble getting their size that they stop wearing hats except in very bad weather. The result is that the sales statistics do not properly express the distribution of hat sizes.

And when I lived in Washington during the second World War, I heard another story of statistics that miscarried. The Women's Army Corps had been formed and they needed shoes, of course. Purchases were made in accordance with the statistics supplied by manufacturers of women's shoes, and it turned out that they had bought too many small sizes. Because the manufacturer's statistics were, naturally, based on sales volume . . . and in this case the sales volumes did *not* reflect the distribution of foot size!

But aside from such comparatively minor exceptions the bean curve is a useful statistical device.

CHAPTER XI

THE EARLY DAYS OF THE METRIC SYSTEM

IT MAY BE TRADITIONAL to divide a length called "one foot" into twelve equal parts called inches and then to chop up these inches into halves, quarters and so forth. Or going the other way, it may be traditional to say that three feet make one yard (why not four since the inch gets quartered?) and end up with the traditional but exceedingly clumsy figure of 5280 feet to the mile.

It may also be traditional too to say that one shilling contains twelve pence and that twenty shillings make one pound; merely because at one time in history a pound of gold was worth twenty pounds of silver while one pound of silver bought twelve pounds of copper.[1]

While these things may be traditional they are also quite impractical. Every individual has had to memorize them at one time in his or her life. On the other hand, it needs no time at all to "memorize" that there are 100 cents in the dollar, or that 1000 millimeters make one meter, and 1000 meters make one kilometer. Since most of the household and workshop arithmetic can be carried out in one's head when using the metric system, but needs paper and pencil when carried out in the inch-foot system, the statement that the

[1] For quite a number of centuries a pound of gold was worth thirteen pounds of silver, for no other reason than that gold was assigned to the sun and silver to the moon and that there are thirteen lunar periods to one year, or solar period.

metric system will win out eventually does not even deserve the label "prediction."

But how did it start and why?

The "why" begins with the fact that in, say, 1700 there was no system at all.

If this statement makes you think that each country had its own "pound," and "foot" and "mile" you are only partly right. In actual fact, it was not each country, but each province; and sometimes the northern part of a province used one set of measurements while the southern part of the province used another one. And the cities, being rich, were much too proud to use the rural measurements of the surrounding countryside, so they had their own.

The country that was best off in this chaos was England. There one system was used throughout by royal decree. But in France there was no such uniformity; in the northern part of the country alone the pound had twenty-one different values, depending on where you happened to be. As for measures for grain, not less than three hundred different kinds have been compiled by patient historians. Their relationships were sometimes simple, as when a city council might decree that the city unit for grain was three of the units of the surrounding countryside.

But sometimes the relationships were anything but simple. In fact they were sometimes so complicated that a mathematician had to be called in, as was the case in 1626 when the council of the City of Ulm called on the great Johannes Kepler to straighten out their measurements. The merchants could never agree on the length of a "shoe" and the question of how much grain constituted a "bucket" often had the result that the suppliers and customers flung actual buckets at

each other. Kepler accepted the job for two reasons. One was that the mathematical aspects of the problem intrigued him. The other was that the city paid him.

The final outcome was the "Kettle of Ulm," a metal container which combined all the customary measurements. They were listed on the outside of the kettle in raised letters, even rhyming. The inside diameter of the kettle was one ell, its depth was two shoes, its capacity "one honest bucket." The weight of the kettle, when empty, was 4½ units; when full of water it was 7 units. And now we come to the problem of the grain measure: if you filled the kettle 64 times with grain you had 90 measures!

If one reads that in those days money changers and merchants coped with the endless varieties of silver and of gold coins by just weighing them it looks at first glance as if at least the money changers had found a useful shortcut, based on the fact that a pound of silver is a pound of silver, and a pound of gold is a pound of gold. Well, yes. But which pound? The pound of London, or that of Strasbourg (which was less), or that of Hamburg (which the English then called Hamborough and which was .95 of the London pound), or that of Leipzig, which was 1.15 of the London pound?

No wonder that, in 1704, the Englishman John Harris compiled a book called *Lexicon Technicum* which contained endless tables of how the pound of Calcutta, Rotterdam, etc. compared with that of England; other long tables compared the foot of the various countries. Glancing over these tables now, one sees with a good deal of astonishment that the "Spanish foot" was the same as the English, but the "Toledo foot" was shorter (see Table) while, on the other hand, the Toledo pound was the same as the English. (There seems to have been no "Spanish pound.")

COMPARISON OF THE POUND AVOIRDUPOIS AND THE FOOT WITH OTHER "POUNDS" AND "FEET" IN 1704.*

	Pound	Foot
London	1.000	1.000
Paris	.930	1.063
Amsterdam	.930	.942
Leyden	.960	1.033
Antwerp	.980	.946
Strasbourg	.930	.920
Bremen	.940	.964
Cologne	.970	.954
Frankfurt on the Main	.930	.948
Toledo	1.000	.899

* According to the *Lexicon Technicum* by John Harris.

But the internal confusion was greatest in France. Many Frenchmen felt that, if the King of England could decree uniform measurements throughout his realm, the King of France should do the same. The French, at the time, had a system of making complaints and suggestions. The documents bore the name of *Cahiers de doleances* (writs of grievances) and they seem to have contained complaints about the lack of uniform measurements almost every year. The earliest known was in a *cahier* of 1576. By about 1785, the government in Paris decided that a reform should be considered. Reading about a two-century interval one is reminded of the famous lines—

> the government,
> the truth to tell,
> did nothing in particular,
> but did it very well!

But it was not just a case of indifference and procrastination. To say that things are confused and that a reform is needed is one thing. Making useful suggestions for a reform

is something else. The French government—ultimately the king—seems to have felt that the suggestions were incomplete in themselves. At any event that they were not definite enough to base decrees and laws on them.

The English had taken their measurements from the human body. The "foot" was an actual foot; that is, it was the average of the foot lengths of a dozen grown men, picked at random (or so the story goes). Now it so happened that 36 barleycorns "from the center of an ear" made one foot; therefore the "barleycorn" became the subdivision of an inch, with three barleycorn to the inch. Later on most artisans decided that halving and quartering the inch was easier, so only bootmakers continued to use the barleycorn as the smaller unit—a practice still continued by shoe manufacturers in England and in the United States. A difference of one size means a difference of one barleycorn, or one third of an inch, in length. It also happened that a piece of rope stretched from fingertip to fingertip across the chest of a man (a "fathom") was very closely six feet, and one half of that became a yard.

The official English measurements, then, were based on the human body, and the measures of other areas and cities probably were too. But the French scientists did not wish to follow this pattern. The dimensions of the human body were too variable. Basing a set of official measures on the size of the planet Earth was more to their liking, since the size of the planet would not change. That was, of course, true enough; the problem was that the size of the planet was not accurately known.

It is not surprising that the first man to propose using the planet Earth as a standard was an astronomer. He was Jacques Cassini, the son of the more famous Giovanni Domenico Cassini, and for that reason often called Cassini the

Second. He suggested in 1720 that the standard foot should be the hundredth part of one second of arc of a meridian. The French Academy thought this a fine and logical suggestion, which only had the one drawback that the various attempts to measure the length of a meridian showed rather poor agreement. About thirty years later another French scientist, the mathematician and astronomer Charles-Marie de la Condamine, came with another suggestion which would be easier to carry out in practice.

Galileo Galilei had been the first to notice that the time required for a pendulum to complete one swing depended on the length of the pendulum. In reality the time required depends on two factors, namely the length of the pendulum and the latitude, but Galileo did not know that. It was suspected by the astronomer Jean Picard that latitude might be a factor involved. But Picard made the general suggestion that a pendulum of a length resulting in a period of one second would be a useful basis for linear measurements.

The length of the seconds pendulum, it may be mentioned at this point, is 39.01 inches, or 99.09 centimeters; this is the standard figure, which requires a correction for the latitude.

To get away from the need for corrections, de la Condamine suggested the length of the seconds pendulum *at the equator* as the unit for linear measurement.

So these were the two suggestions, either a fraction of the length of the meridian, or else the length of the seconds pendulum. But both still had to be determined.

Along with the problem of finding a standard length which would not vary—and which could be re-established in case a catastrophe of some kind destroyed the first standard—there was the problem of subdivision of the standard. Thinking in dozens was customary; as we have seen the foot was divided

into a dozen inches or into three dozen barleycorns. But the dozen was not the only sub-unit of super-unit in use. In some places the foot was divided into eighths, and in Germany things like eggs or hard rolls were sold not by the dozen, but by the *Mandel* which was 15 units. To make things worse the Germans had the "peasant's mandel" in addition; it consisted of 16 units. (Remember the "baker's dozen.")

A dozen may be superior to ten because it can be divided by 2, 3, 4 and 6, while ten can only be divided by 2 and 5, but it so happens that we have ten fingers. A division into ten sub-units is therefore easier to visualize, at least for the beginner. The man who was the first to advocate subdivision into tenths was the Dutch mathematician Simon Stevin, military engineer to Count Maurits of Nassau. Stevin was not concerned with the measurements themselves or their origin and accuracy; he just advocated subdivision into decimal fractions. In order to find a larger audience he wrote his book twice, once in Latin and once in French. Both versions were printed in Leyden in 1585. The title of the French version was *La Disme*, and the English translation by Robert Norton (published in 1608) was called *Disme: The Art of Tenths, or, Decimall Arithmeticke.*

The word *disme* means "tenth" and is related to "tithe." At one time it was the name of an American coin, the Half Dismes and Dismes between 1792 and 1800, later spelled "dimes."

Apparently Simon Stevin's book in its various editions convinced everyone—with the exception of the Master of the Royal Mint—of the superiority of decimal fractions, for the French Academy decided from the outset that this is what they would use in carrying out the mandate from the National Assembly to create a new system of weights and measures. The National Assembly had recommended the length

of the seconds pendulum as a suitable (and repeatable) physical constant, but it had not said anything about decimal
fractions.

But while the Academy decided on decimal fractions it
also decided that the meridian would be superior to the
seconds pendulum as a standard. It recommended in 1791
that the ten millionth part of the distance from the pole to
the equator should be the new unit of measurement, the
meter. The National Assembly accepted the recommenda-
tion. And then the hard work of measuring began.

In the meantime the savants had to fight with words.
The unit was to be the meter (in French *mètre*) and a
tenth of a meter was a decimeter. A tenth of a decimeter,
or a hundredth of a meter, was obviously a centimeter. The
tenth part of a centimeter was a millimeter—the word means
a thousandth of a meter.

Going the other way, a term meaning a thousand meters
was needed. The Greek word *chilioi* suggested itself, in spite
of two drawbacks. In Greek letters the "ch" was the letter
chi, which looks like this: χ. But the letter χ, considered
as a numeral, meant 600. However, the Greeks themselves
had often used the χ to mean 1000, as an abbreviation of
the word *chilioi*.

One thing somewhat disturbing to Frenchmen was that
all classical scholars were agreed that the *chi* was a guttural
and Frenchmen, for no better reason that they cannot pro-
nounce them easily, are opposed to gutturals. But somebody
saved the day by discovering that the Ionian dialect of Greek
used a *kappa* instead of the *chi*—the Ionians apparently were
opposed to gutturals too—and the name of the unit of 1000
meters became the kilometer.

Now the unit of linear measure was to be the ten millionth part of the distance from a pole to the equator. This

could be determined without much difficulty from the figure provided by Nicolas-Louis de Lacaille, who derived the length of one degree of the meridian under 45 latitude as 57,027 *toises,* each *toise* being six feet Parisian. (Take it from there . . . if you have absolutely nothing else to do.) But the new system also was to include weights, and the unit of weight was to be the weight of a unit volume of distilled water weighed in a vacuum chamber at the temperature of melting ice. The name chosen for this unit was *gravet.*

Later on the unit volume was chosen as one cubic centimeter, and the temperature was shifted from that of melting ice to 4 degrees centigrade because at that temperature water shows its greatest density. Finally the name of this unit weight became *gram,* with kilogram for a thousand of these units and ton (metric ton) for a thousand kilograms.

Everything would have been fine if France had not become a republic in the meantime. Now the work of establishing the new system was under a new commission. Of course it had the name of *Commission temporaire des Poids & Mésures républicains,* the Temporary Commission for Republican Weights and Measures. The system that had been meant for everybody in all countries had now become the "System of the Republic," just as they concocted a "Calendar of the Republic" which was finally abandoned by Napoleon to the jubilation of everybody. Whether the French revolutionaries actually intended the new system to be for France only is quite unlikely, but the title page of the official book introducing the system sounded as if this were the case.

The title page read (the sign/indicates that a new line began on the page): *Instruction/sur/Les Mésures/déduites/de la Grandeur de la Terre,/uniformes/Pour Toute la République/ et/sur les calculs relatifs/a leur division decimale.* In English:

Instructions on the Measurements derived from the size of the earth, uniform for the whole republic, with tables in decimal fractions.

With such a title page, the King of England, the King of Prussia, the Czar of all the Russians and every other king or prince could not only suspect that this might not be suitable for his country, he almost had to come to the conclusion that it should be forbidden in his country. As a matter of fact, because of these (purely accidental) political implications the new system made headway very slowly. It made headway slowly in France too. The system became legal in December 1799 and the First Consul of the Republic Napoleon Bonaparte made it compulsory in 1801. But in 1837, several governments later, a law had to be passed imposing fines on recalcitrant silk and wine merchants (among others) who did not use the metric system exclusively beginning January 1, 1840.

By now the metric system is all but universal. The Russians adopted it in 1918, and in the two countries which are still holding out, the British Commonwealth is considering its introduction and in the United States, it is at least legal. In the United States, as a matter of fact, the yard and pound, etc., are defined in terms of the metric system, so that a housewife buying two yards of fabric is actually buying according to the metric system, though she is not likely to know the fact unless her husband happens to be a lawyer or a scientist.

What opposition to the metric system remains is usually based on invested capital. A factory will say that it has X million dollars invested in non-metric machinery, and even though these machines could be converted it would not do any good, because the raw material, bar stock, etc., comes in non-metric dimensions from the rolling mill. And the rolling mill says,

of course, that they have X million dollars invested in *their* machinery.

It is an opposition which will slowly dwindle away. But as far as argumentation is concerned it is certainly superior to that of a now forgotten society which existed in 1879 (and for a few years after) in Boston.

The background for this society had been the attempt of Charles Piazzi Smyth, Astronomer Royal for Scotland, to find all kinds of "cosmic secrets" in the Great Pyramid. Assuming that the number of the days of the year had to be hidden in the base line of the Great Pyramid, Piazzi Smyth divided the base line into 365.2422 parts and named the unit thus derived the "pyramid meter." This he then divided into 25 parts to obtain the "pyramid inch," which turned out to be almost the same as the English inch.

Piazzi Smyth quickly concluded that the English inch was just a faintly corrupted "pyramid inch." Hence the English system of measurement by inches really went back to ancient Egypt. By 1870 most of those who played around with the dimensions of the Great Pyramid had also concluded that the pyramid had been divinely inspired in the most literal meaning of the term. Hence the inch was sacred. Hence it was necessary to form a society with the ultimate purpose of outlawing the "atheist metric system." James Abram Garfield, later president of the United States, was an active supporter of this movement against the meter.

The movement did not last long.

Besides, the metric system had been legalized in 1866.

CHAPTER XII

TOO MUCH IMAGINATION

TO THE BEST OF MY KNOWLEDGE the flying saucer myth never passed through the iron curtain, except for being ridiculed in the official Russian press. But that does not mean that the Russians are not addicted to the hunting of spurious mysteries too. Contrary to a fairly widespread belief, Soviet censorship does not interfere in such matters as long as the mysteries, real or imagined, have nothing to do with political dogma. Authors can even quote the Bible, provided it is treated as a historical work without religious significance.

For example the *Literaturnaya Gazyeta* ("Literary Gazette"), which once upon a time ran articles bitterly denouncing science fiction, printed an article in which the destruction of Sodom was "tentatively explained" as the result of a nuclear explosion, and the damage done Lot's wife was blindness from having watched the explosion at close range! The same article explained the so-called Baalbek Verandah in Lebanon—a large area paved with big stone slabs—as an ancient spaceport, used by cosmonauts from another planet.

But the favorite exercise ground for untrammeled Russian imaginations is a place in the Soviet Union itself, an area in Central Siberia where a natural catastrophe took place in 1908. In astronomical literature this catastrophe goes under the name of the "Great Siberian Meteor of 1908," or the Podkamennaya Tunguska Meteorite.

The facts of the case can be quickly told: A few minutes after 7 A.M. on June 30, 1908, observers in Central Siberia saw a fiery body come up over the southern horizon. It looked more blinding than the sun which was in the sky at the same time, and moved rapidly almost due North. Shortly thereafter a "pillar of fire" could be seen shooting upward. An enormous black cloud followed. A number of explosions were heard in quick succession, and at least one witness felt a shock wave in the ground which he described as being "like a single wave in the sea." Barographs as far west as London registered a shock wave in the atmosphere but seismographs outside of Russia did not register any ground shock.

On the following day meteorologists in Asia and Europe noticed "noctilucent clouds," silvery-looking clouds at extreme altitudes. All of them were immediately reminded of the noctilucent clouds that had hovered in the upper atmosphere for several years after the explosion of the volcano Rakata on Krakatoa in 1883. But when Krakatoa blew up, shock waves in the air had circled the globe several times, a wave in the ocean had been detected on the coast of California and all seismographs had quivered.

Here only a comparatively small aerial shockwave had preceded the noctilucent clouds. It could not have been a major volcanic catastrophe. At least one German meteorologist concluded that the "disturbance in the atmosphere," as he called it, had probably been caused by a large meteorite. In Russia scientists seem to have concluded that there had been an earthquake in Central Siberia. Probably they were happy that it had struck in a virtually uninhabited area. Tentatively it was concluded that the earthquake had been near the small city of Kansk. There was no official action.

It was not until 1920 that a Russian scientist, Professor L. A. Kulik, having convinced himself that the "earthquake"

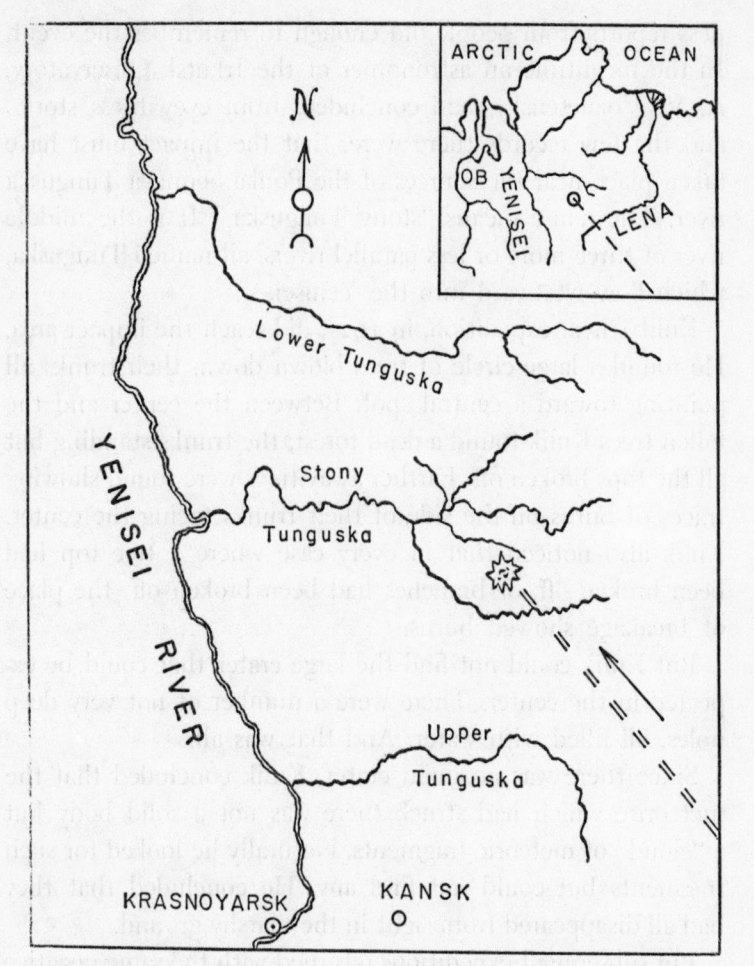

FIG. 40. Sketch map of the impact area of the Stony Tunguska meteorite.

must have been a meteorite impact, tried to find the place where it had struck.

His tiny and severely underfinanced expedition accomplished only two things. He proved that the meteorite had *not* landed near Kansk, and he collected a number of eyewit-

ness reports from people old enough to remember the event. In the meantime an astronomer of the Irkutsk Observatory, A. V. Voznesensky, had concluded, from eyewitness stories and the few records there were, that the impact must have taken place near the sources of the Podkamennaya Tunguska river. The name means "stony Tunguska." It is the middle river of three more or less parallel rivers, all named Tunguska, which flow westward into the Yenisei.

Kulik's next expedition, in 1927, did reach the impact area. He found a large circle of trees blown down, their trunks all pointing toward a central spot. Between the center and the fallen trees Kulik found a dead forest, the trunks standing but all the tops broken off. Farther away trees were found showing traces of burns on the side of their trunks facing the center. Kulik also noticed that in every case where a tree top had been broken off, or branches had been broken off, the place of breakage showed burns.

But Kulik could not find the large crater that could be expected in the center. There were a number of not very deep holes, all filled with water. And that was all.

Since there was no main crater, Kulik concluded that the meteorite which had struck there was not a solid body but a "cloud" of meteoric fragments. Naturally he looked for such fragments but could not find any. He concluded that they had all disappeared from sight in the marshy ground.

But subsequent expeditions returned with the same negative results. Gradually the Podkamennaya Tunguska meteorite became a mystery. Here you had an area which bore all the signs of a major impact, you had eyewitness stories corroborating this evidence. And you could not find a single trace of the meteorite itself!

Since there was absolutely no way of getting around the evidence only one conclusion was possible: the meteorite

must have been of a kind which completely disappeared afterwards.

Leonid Kulik, who personally believed that it had been an iron meteorite, made more expeditions into the roadless and swampy area, without great success. Still no main crater—it is now definite that there is none—and still no fragments of the meteorite. Only a story by one of the natives of the area, the Tunguses, that another native had told him that a third one had shown him a piece of metal which looked like silver. By 1938 the first aerial photographs were taken, but either the equipment was wrong for the purpose or the photographer had no experience in taking pictures from the air. The pictures were so poor that they could be called worthless. Then came the second world war and investigation stopped. Moreover Kulik, who in spite of his age (he was then 58) had volunteered for military duty, was wounded and taken prisoner by the Germans. He died in the prison camp.

By the time Kulik made his last expedition, 1938–39, at least one new theory about the disappearing meteorite had been formed and was discussed for a while. If the meteorite had been contraterrene matter everything could be explained.[1] Contraterrene matter would react violently with normal matter, liberating enormous amounts of energy by a mutual particle-for-particle annihilation. Since this reaction would, of course, start in the atmosphere the unusual brightness of the

[1] The concept of contraterrene matter was started in 1930 by the English physicist Paul Dirac who became convinced that there should be an electron carrying a positive charge. This so-called "anti-particle" was discovered in 1932 by the American physicist Carl David Anderson. It has the mass of an electron but carries a positive electrical charge. Normal electrons carry a negative charge. It was logical to expand the concept of anti-particles and to assume matter consisting of negatively charged nuclei, surrounded by positrons. Such "contraterrene matter" and normal matter could not exist side by side, but there may be whole solar systems or even galaxies of contraterrene matter.

body would be accounted for. The mutual annihilation of matter would release enough energy to account for the observed devastation. And, of course, the meteorite would disappear down to its last atom, taking an equal mass of earth matter along. The site of the impact would be strongly radioactive afterwards—but the impact had taken place in 1908 and the first investigation was not until 1927. And Kulik's party had not carried any Geiger counters, so that they could not check on traces of radioactivity that might still have been there.

By 1947 another expedition to the Podkamennaya Tunguska was delayed by a most curious coincidence. In eastern Siberia, a few hundred miles north of Vladivostok, a large meteorite was seen to fall and all the scientific talent was rushed to the Sikhôté-Alin mountains. It was a large iron meteorite, all right. It had broken up during the passage through the atmosphere and produced over 120 craters of all sizes, the largest about 90 feet across. But there was no mystery about the Sikhôté-Alin meteorite, though it delayed another expedition to the Tunguska.

At that point a Russian engineer and science writer by the name of Aleksandr Kazântsev had entered the debate. His thesis was that the meteorite of 1908 had not been a meteorite at all, but a spaceship.

Kazântsev did not hesitate to elaborate. It had been a huge atomic-powered interstellar ship which had approached our solar system, first investigating the outer planets and finally approaching Earth, which clearly proved to be inhabited. The captain of the ship, circling the earth several times, decided to find an uninhabited area to land so as not to harm the inhabitants of Earth inadvertently. But as he entered the atmosphere for a landing in Siberia something went wrong. Possibly the aliens had misjudged the density of the earth's atmosphere. The ship heated up and became uncontrollable,

and on touching the ground, or just above it, the atomic engine exploded, vaporizing the ship, flattening out the forest below and setting the taiga on fire.

An atomic explosion of that type, Kazântsev maintained, would explain not only the observed phenomena but also the absence of any meteoritic material. Russian astronomers were presumably still shaking their heads when Kazântsev received the support of another science writer by the name of Boris Liapûnov.

Between them they seem to have succeeded in convincing a fair percentage of the Russian reading public that an interstellar expedition crashed in Siberia in 1908.

By 1957 a careful analysis of soil samples from the site, collected by Kulik, was carried out. Small globules of meteoric iron were discovered and found to contain 7 per cent of nickel, 0.7 per cent of cobalt and traces of germanium and copper. This is a rather typical composition of iron meteorites—and it should be stated right here that this meteoric iron may well have no connection with the fall of 1908 at all. Such tiny bits of meteoric iron can be found anywhere on Earth if you search long enough; the daily infall of meteoric matter is now estimated to be around 1000 tons per day. The globules found may thus have fallen at any time in history.

But Kazântsev, in a manner reminiscent of our flying saucer "researchers," pounced on the composition. Iron plus nickel plus cobalt? Obviously a piece of the alloy which formed the tough outer skin of the spaceship. Traces of copper? Surely they must have had electrical equipment on board, requiring copper wires. He could have said the same if the traces had been traces of silver. And germanium? Why not? Electronic gear requires semi-conductors which can be germanium compounds. The explosion, according to Kazântsev, took place before the ship touched the ground, therefore the trees di-

rectly below were merely stripped of their crowns (and ignited) while the trees farther away, struck by the blast at an angle, were knocked down. The "pillar of fire" topped by a large cloud could only have been an atomic explosion, Kazántsev declared. (This happens not to be the case. You can get very similar clouds from any large explosion.) And the silvery clouds noticed by the meteorologists were the explosion débris, luminous because atomic disintegration was still going on. (Yet the clouds caused by the Krakatoa catastrophe looked the same and Krakatoa's blow-up holds no atomic mystery.) To finish up his case, Kazántsev dragged in an alleged native legend, namely that the god Ogda burned Tunguses with "invisible fire." Obviously, he wrote, some natives approached the blast site so soon after the event that local atomic fallout burned and killed them.

One more supporter of the spaceship theory who turned up in 1958 was the airplane designer A. Y. Manotskov.

Manotskov had checked on the eyewitness reports gathered mainly by Kulik in 1921 and 1927 and tried to calculate both the flightpath and the velocity of the body. Eyewitness reports, if they state the position of the observer and cite landmarks, can give a fairly accurate picture of the direction of a flightpath but are absolutely valueless when it comes to speed of travel. The speed of a low-flying slow body and of a high-flying fast body can look exactly the same—as anybody living near an airport can see for himself, when comparing the apparent speed of a small executive plane coming in for a landing and a jet passing overhead at 26,000 feet. Manotskov arrived at the conclusion that the "meteorite" moved at the rate of only about 1500 miles per hour. But if it was so slow, the observed devastation required a very large body, one well over one kilometer (0.6 miles) in diameter. A

meteorite that size *must* have left débris. Since none had been found it had to be a spaceship.

At about that time Kazântsev made an interesting about-face.

Having read about contraterrene matter—he called it "anti-matter"—he said that one did not need to assume that the ship's engine exploded. It was at least equally likely that the ship came from a planet consisting of anti-matter, and that its captain and crew never guessed that the matter composing Earth was of the opposite kind. With that theory Kazântsev agreed with western ideas that it could have been a contraterrene meteorite. He substituted a contraterrene spaceship for a natural body. Apparently he did not notice that his acceptance of contraterrene matter contradicted his earlier conclusions drawn from the composition of the meteoritic globules found on the site. If his alien ship had germanium semi-conductors that would have been contraterrene germanium and nothing would have been left to analyze.

The Soviet Academy of Sciences paid for another expedition in 1957, headed by Professor Kirill P. Florénsky, who saw to it that there were Geiger counters among the equipment. The radioactivity of the soil was found to be perfectly normal—which admittedly might well be the case after nearly half a century, especially since there were no figures about the radioactivity of that area before the catastrophe. And Florénsky's expedition definitely established the absence of a major crater. Now everything was what it had been like thirty years earlier: all the evidence of a major impact, but no crater and no meteoritic fragments. The only new item added was the proved absence of above-normal radioactivity.

While Florénsky was still in Siberia, the astronomer and space travel expert Ariy Shternfeld made a few devastating

comments about the professional ability of Kazántsev's spaceship captain. As our earth orbits the sun the area which has
dawn is the "front side." Since the impact took place at 7
o'clock in the morning, Siberia was still on the "front side"
of the moving earth. Hence Earth and spaceship collided
head-on.

Any spaceship captain worth his four stripes (or just one
and a half of them) would trail a moving planet on which
he wished to make planetfall, which means that he would
land between, say, 9 and 10 P.M. of local time of the landing area.

This simple fact had been overlooked by Kazántsev, by
Liapúnov, by Manotskov and by everybody else who had
written and orated about the "spaceship crash of 1908."

Well, is there an answer at all?

Remember that the main and at first glance somewhat disturbing result of all the facts is that the meteorite had to
"disappear" completely. This requirement, in fact, was the
main reason why a contraterrene meteorite was postulated by
some. Anybody who wishes to believe this may safely do so.
Nothing speaks against this possibility. But there are others.

Supposing the meteorite had just been a hundred thousand
tons of water and ice. It would have completely disappeared
during the same summer and would have caused just as much
devastation. But the pillar of fire and the burning of the
taiga speaks against it. A sufficiently hard impact of a very
large lump of ice would produce temperatures high enough
to ignite wood; but it would also smother the fire at once.

However, there is one type of cosmic body which would do
everything the Tunguska meteorite did and would not necessarily smother a fire set by its impact, but it would completely disappear just the same. This body is a comet.

Some thirty years ago the astronomical concept of a comet

was that it consisted of a loose accumulation of cosmic matter holding a large amount of gases—like ammonia, methane and ordinary water. Then Fred L. Whipple showed that things had to be the other way round. A loose cloud of meteoric matter could not hold enough gas. A comet had to consist in the main of frozen gases, probably holding some particles of cosmic dust imbedded in it.

The impact of a small comet would produce all the phenomena observed in Siberia. And it would completely disappear: the ammonia and methane would mingle with the atmosphere (the methane probably burning up) while the water would also go into the atmosphere as more water vapor.

The Russians have accepted this explanation—the Russian astronomers, that is, not Kazántsev and company. The combustion of methane, of course, just produces carbon dioxide and water vapor ($CH_4 + 2O_2 = CO_2 + 2H_2O$) which would be undistinguishable; but the other frozen gases of which a comet is likely to consist might leave a chemical residue in the soil.

There is a chance that chemical compounds were formed which, though well known, are unlikely to exist in that type of soil. Russian chemists started such an investigation in 1963 but since nothing has been heard about it, the investigation probably was fruitless as any reasonably skeptical person would have predicted.

In the meantime Russian astronomers have done something else. If the meteorite of 1908 was a small comet it was possible that this comet had been observed at an earlier occasion. Looking at likely comet orbits might furnish an answer. If there was one that could be expected to be near the earth's orbit in 1908 and failed to show up it would be the culprit. This investigation was fruitless too, but the orbit calculations

turned up a fact that made the experts shudder in retrospect. If that orbit had been just slightly different so that the earth had had another five hours to turn eastward, the comet would have caused the greatest catastrophe of recorded history: it would have made impact in the middle of the Russian capital, St. Petersburg!

CHAPTER XIII

THE GALACTIC GIANTS

Um Erden wandeln Monde,	Moons go around the Earths
Erden um Sonnen,	the Earths go 'round the suns,
Aller Sonnen Heere wandeln	and all the hosts of suns
Um eine grosse Sonne.	circle a giant sun.

(F. G. Klopstock, 1724–1803)

WHEN THE GERMAN POET Friedrich Gottlieb Klopstock wrote the ode from which these lines are taken, he did not indulge in poetic imagery only. Actually he just wrote down what many astronomers and philosophers of his time believed to be true. Klopstock's direct source was probably Immanuel Kant's *General Natural History and Theory of the Heavens*, published for the first time in 1755.

Immanuel Kant—he happened to be born in the same year as Klopstock and survived him by one year—not only believed in a "central sun" of the Milky Way, he even thought that we could see it in the sky. Kant's candidate for the role of the "central sun" was Sirius, the brightest star of the northern sky. Kant's reasoning, as usual, was logical and clear.

Since the Milky Way does not have the same width all the way around but looks wider in the area between Cygnus and Sagittarius, it follows that our sun is not in the center, but is closer to this section of the Milky Way. Sirius, on the

other hand, is in a position that could be the center; and it is also the brightest star. Of course, in order to be the central sun, it would have to be larger by far than any other star. Shouldn't this fact be immediately apparent to the eye? Kant explained why it doesn't have to be so obvious: "even if it (Sirius) were 10,000 times as large as our sun, the apparent brightness and size would be the same if it were a hundred times farther away." Since the distance to Sirius, or to any other star, was not known at the time, nobody could argue with the supposition that Sirius might be the central sun of the Milky Way.

For a full century Kant's opinion was quoted as something that was probably correct even though it could neither be proved nor disproved. But around the middle of the nineteenth century the distance to Sirius had been determined— after a few corrections—as being only 8.7 light years. This calculation enabled astronomers to make fairly correct guesses about the size of Sirius. It was larger than our sun, but not much larger, and many times as luminous. In short: Sirius could not be the central sun, but that did not mean that there was no central sun.

By 1880, say, the idea of a central sun had been, as somebody phrased it, "reluctantly abandoned." Another forty years later it became clear that the Milky Way galaxy was about six times larger than had been assumed, since the galactic center and everything "behind" it—from our point of view—is hidden by enormous clouds of cosmic dust and gas. At that moment the idea of a central sun could have been revived on the grounds that since we cannot see the galactic center we cannot say whether there is a central sun or not. But the general progress of astronomical research prevented this argument from being uttered. It was already clear that certain objects in the sky were other galaxies and while many of them

showed a definite nucleus where suns are more densely packed than in their arms, none showed a central sun.

Nobody is looking for a central sun of overwhelming mass and gravitational might anymore, but a related question is still very much alive. Our galaxy is an aggregation of perhaps 100,000 *million* stars of varying sizes. One of them must be the largest. Which one is it and how large is it?

Slowly now, we cannot answer that question because only about one sixth of our galaxy can be directly observed. Alright then, which is the largest star in the observable portion of our galaxy?

Well, yes—now that is an interesting question. Too bad that it cannot be answered without first asking a few counter-questions. That word "largest" may be good enough when it comes to light bulbs, cigars or elephants. It is not good enough, meaning precise enough, when it comes to stars. Do you mean the brightest star, the one with the greatest luminosity? Or do you mean the star with the greatest mass, the one that would weigh most if it could be placed on a scale? Or do you mean the star with the greatest volume, the one that occupies more cubic miles of space than any other? These are three different classifications and they do not go together.

Since stars are by definition self-luminous objects we'll look for brilliance first. As seen from earth, the crown goes to Sirius, it sends us more than twice as much light as any other star we can see.

But that only means that Sirius is the brightest star in our sky, it does not mean that it is the brightest star in the observable portion of the galaxy. It is self-evident that a much brighter star which is also much farther away will look dimmer to our eyes. To get rid of the difficulty caused by the very considerable differences in distances a simplifying convention had to be introduced. It consisted of agreeing on a

standard distance; the distance chosen was 10 parsecs or
32.59 light years. The magnitude of a star is described as if
it were that distance away, and it is called the absolute magnitude. The magnitude that we do see and which makes Sirius
the brightest star in our sky is the apparent magnitude.

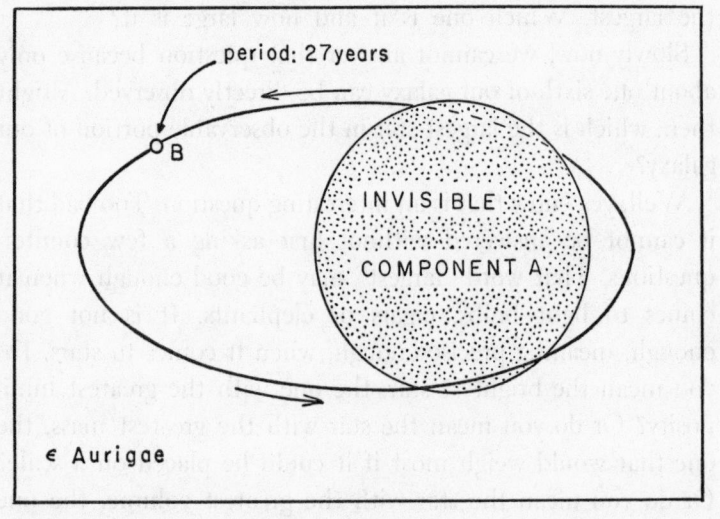

FIG. 41. The two components of epsilon Aurigae, drawn to scale,
in the position they occupied in 1951.

Just to clear up the terminology it has to be added that
two other kinds of magnitude are mentioned in astronomical
literature. One is the visual magnitude which is the same as
the apparent magnitude for visual observations. But stars that
radiate a great deal of blue and violet light look brighter
on the photographic plate than they do to the eye and here,
of course, the term photographic magnitude is used.

For our discussion the photographic magnitude can be neglected. We will deal only with the "apparent (visual) magnitude" and mainly with the "absolute magnitude" the visual
magnitude as it would be if seen from a distance of 10 parsecs.

If you deal with absolute magnitudes only the relative luminosities of the stars can be expressed simply in terms of the luminosity of our sun. A star that is as luminous as our sun, no matter how faint it looks because of a long distance, would be said to have the luminosity "1."

But let us look at a few examples.

Sirius has a luminosity of 26, that is to say that it is 26 times as bright as the sun. The nearest other star, *alpha* Centauri happens to be a binary, its brighter component, *alpha* Centauri A has a luminosity of 1.1, it is just a little brighter than our sun. The other component, *alpha* Centauri B, is much dimmer, its luminosity is only 0.2. Vega's luminosity is 50, that of Capella is 150, and that of Aldebaran is 90. The star *beta* Centauri, second brightest star in the constellation of the Centaur, has a surprisingly great luminosity, namely 3000; but unlike *alpha* Centauri *beta* Centauri is 300 light years or 91 parsecs distant. Deneb, about 200 parsecs away, has a luminosity of about 10,000, Rigel, about 166 parsecs distant, has a luminosity of 18,000, and Canopus, 200 parsecs away, has a luminosity of 80,000. If the earth were suddenly placed in an orbit 100 million miles from Canopus, all land life on the hemisphere pointing at Canopus would be killed instantly and the oceans would have boiled away before the earth had time to rotate once on its axis.

A close runner-up of Canopus is *ypsilon* Sagittarii. To the naked eye it is just a fourth magnitude star at an estimated distance of about 9000 light years or 3200 parsecs. Its luminosity is somewhere between 50,000 and 70,000 times that of our sun. Naturally such estimates cannot be precise; we simply cannot know how much of the light is absorbed by so-called "empty" space during a 9000 year journey. It is entirely possible that *ypsilon* Sagittarii has the same lumi-

nosity as Canopus. At any event these two, at the moment, share first place as regards true luminosity among the stars in the observable region of our galaxy.

Though this survey is restricted to the one sixth of our own galaxy that can be observed visually, one exception has to be made.

Our galaxy has two satellite galaxies collectively known as the Magellanic Clouds. The larger of the Magellanic Clouds contains numerous clusters of stars, often imbedded in nebulosities. Many hot and bright blue-white giants of the type of Rigel are present. It is generally assumed that Rigel type giants are the result of a recent "feeding" with cosmic dust due to a passage through a dust cloud. Since space inside the Greater Magellanic Cloud is quite dusty, all this goes together quite well. But in a cluster of the cloud which is labelled NGC 1910 there is a supergiant surpassing anything that we can see in our section of the galaxy. It is the star called S Doradus. Because of the distance of 160,000 light years S Doradus is not visible to the naked eye, yet it is the most luminous star known.

It is a variable, with an absolute luminosity ranging from 8.2 at minimum to 9.4 at maximum. This means that its average luminosity is *one million times* that of our sun! If it is a single star its diameter might be as large as 200 million miles. But it may be a binary. Sergei Gaposchkin has suggested that it might be a system of two blue-white supergiants eclipsing each other during a 40-year period. It has also been suggested that S Doradus was, a comparatively short time ago, a double supernova which is now fading.

If S Doradus is a single star and if it follows the rules derived from our "neighborhood stars," its lifetime, at the present rate of energy expenditure, would be only 3000 years.

As far as the more luminous objects that have been dubbed

"quasars"—a contraction of the original designation "quasi-stellar objects"—are concerned, I'm going to postpone any discussion until the time we know something about them.

Determining the surface temperature of a star is relatively easy with modern instrumentation.

Measuring a star's apparent magnitude and calculating its true luminosity does not present any special difficulties and if all these factors are known it is easy to calculate the surface area of a star and to derive its diameter from the surface area.

But while every star that throws radiation into space advertises its temperature, composition and size, very many stars succeed in retaining a secret, namely their mass and density. As a matter of fact there is no way of determining the mass of a *single* star. Only if the star in question is a component of a binary—or a multiple system—can we find its mass by studying the orbital paths followed by the two stars. Of course in quite a number of cases close guesses can be made. If we have one star where the mass could be determined because it is a component of a binary and we then find another star of the same absolute magnitude and belonging to the same (spectral) class, it is reasonable to assume that this latter star's mass will be about the same as that of the measured star.

Keeping the restriction in mind that, generally speaking, we can know only the masses of binaries we can now ask about the most massive star known.

The answer is: H.D. 47129 in the constellation Monoceros. The letters H.D. stand for "Henry Draper Catalogue," published by Harvard University during the years immediately following the first World War. But H.D. 47129 has a name, too. It is known as Plaskett's Star, after J. S. Plaskett, the director of the Dominion Astrophysical Observatory at Victoria, British Columbia, who proved that this star was a bi-

nary with an orbital period of 14.4 days. The combined mass of the binary turned out to be 180 times the mass of our sun. Both components seem to share this mass equally, or very nearly so, so that each component of Plaskett's star has a mass of 90 times that of the sun. Both also belong to the same spectral type (O₈) and since the density of stars of that spectral type is usually only about 10 per cent of the sun's density they must be large in size too.

If Sir Arthur Eddington is right, the two components of this binary are about as massive as a star can be. He found that a star of a mass greater than about 100 solar masses cannot exist. When that mass is reached the radiation pressure inside the star becomes stronger than the gravitational forces that hold the star together. A star of, say, 150 solar masses would be blown apart by its own radiation pressure.

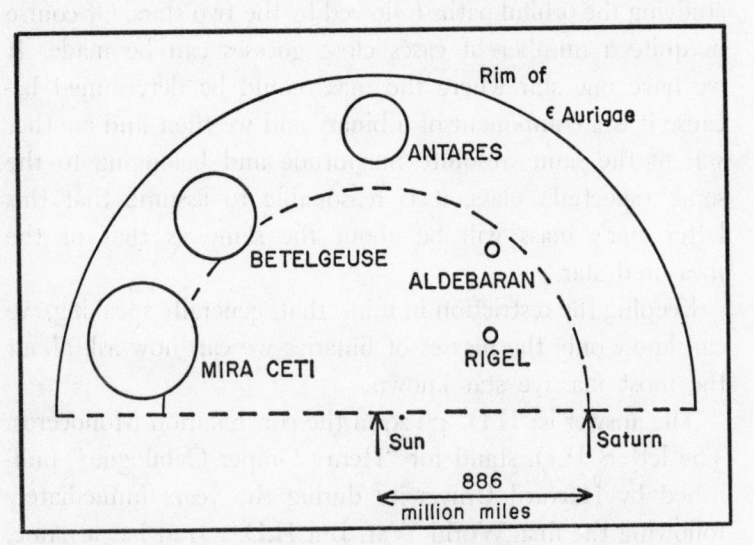

FIG. 42. Rigel is a Blue-white Giant, Aldebaran a Red Giant, Antares, Betelgeuse and Mira Ceti are Red Supergiants, and epsilon Aurigae is in a class by itself which has no name yet. If the sun were in the center of epsilon Aurigae, the planet Saturn would move along the broken line.

So far all known examples conform to Sir Arthur Eddington's calculation, even the largest stars have masses far below the two heavyweights that form Plaskett's Star.

And that brings us to the stars with the greatest volume, collectively known as the Red Giants: Algol, Aldebaran and Arcturus. Algol is a binary consisting of two Red Giants of nearly identical mass and size. Their diameters are 15 times that of the sun, but their masses are only 4 solar masses each. Aldebaran and Arcturus are singles with diameters on the order of 30 solar diameters but their estimated masses are also just 4 solar masses. Antares, Betelgeuse and Mira Ceti are classed as Red Supergiants; their diameters, according to the late Otto Struve, are 300, 400 and 500 solar diameters. But the mass of Antares is estimated as only 10 solar masses, Betelgeuse probably weighs 15 times as much as our sun and Mira Ceti not much more.

But the very largest star of the observable portion of our galaxy is one that has literally never been seen. It is the supergiant *epsilon* Aurigae, with a diameter 3000 times as large as that of the sun—which, incidentally, is 860,000 miles. But if it has never been seen, how do we know that it exists and on what authority can its diameter be given? The answer can almost be guessed: because it is a component of a binary.

The other component of this binary is visible, of course, and the designation *epsilon* Aurigae really belongs to this visible component. It was in 1821 when a German Lutheran pastor by the name of Fritsch, who lived in the old city of Quedlinburg, noticed that it was a variable star. Not realizing that an important discovery was within grasp he did not follow up on his observation and it was Friedrich Wilhelm Ar-

gelander in Bonn who, in 1848, made good visual observations of *epsilon* Aurigae at minimum luminosity. It became clear that *epsilon* Aurigae was a so-called eclipsing variable, which means a star that does not actually change its luminosity periodically as the true variables do. The apparent change is due to the fact that a less luminous star moves in front of its more luminous component, thereby making it look dimmer. Argelander noticed two facts: the orbital period was unusually long and the second component was invisible. As for the latter he probably thought that later and more powerful telescopes would show it.

Other eclipses took place in 1875, 1902 and 1929, all well observed. The last eclipse was in 1955 with the next one due in 1982. The period is 27.1 years, the longest period for an eclipsing binary that is known. Even the eclipse itself is of impressive length; in 1955 it began on June 5. The light of the visible component diminished steadily for 192 days and reached its minimum during the second week of December of that year. It then stayed at minimum for 330 days and needed another 192 days to return to normal, a total eclipse duration of 714 days, or two years minus two weeks and two days. But all the time the smaller component remains visible, shining through the very tenuous large star!

To speak of the luminous member of *epsilon* Aurigae as the "smaller component" is justified only because the term is used in comparison with the larger component. The smaller component is itself a supergiant with a diameter of 250–300 times that of the sun and a mass of about 40 solar masses.

The mass of the large star, ten times the diameter of the smaller companion, is also about 40 solar masses, possibly somewhat less. This has the result that the density is the lowest known of any star, if you took one million cubic miles

of it and compressed it into one cubic mile you would have a substance of the same density as our air at sea level. The surface temperature is at best 1000° centigrade (1832° Fahrenheit) but probably less. It is too cool to be luminous. But, of course, at its center the density and the temperature must be higher. Its core should be luminous but we cannot see it; what little light there is is drowned out by the glare of the bright star. The distance to *epsilon* Aurigae can only be estimated, but is believed to be on the order of 3000 light years.

It has often been said that thoroughness is the cloak of the philosopher and the scientist. Without it he feels naked and does not like to appear in public. Hence a discussion of the galactic giants would be incomplete without at least one quick glance at the galactic midgets.

Just as the question about the largest star has more than one answer, the question about the smallest star does too. And again it is a case of whether "small" is meant to refer to mass, volume or luminosity.

For years the star L 886-6 in Monoceros, discovered by Dr. William J. Luyten, was cited as being the star with the smallest volume. It would need 60,000 such stars to produce as much light as our sun does. The calculated diameter is 2500 miles, only about 340 miles more than the diameter of our moon. But L 886-6 is a White Dwarf, its mass is 1.4 solar masses and the density of its matter is 55 million times the density of water.

But in 1962 Dr. Luyten came up with an even smaller White Dwarf, LP 327-186 in Taurus with a diameter of only about 1000 miles. Its density must be about four times that of the density of L 886-6.

The faintest star known (not a White Dwarf) has a bright-

ness of only one millionth that of the sun. It is a companion
to another faint star, registered as B.D.+4° 4048.[1] It was
discovered by Dr. G. Van Biesbroek and was found to have
an absolute magnitude of 19 in red light, three magnitudes
fainter than the oft quoted faint star Wolf 359.

The lightest known star was announced by Dr. Peter van
de Camp in 1944. Its designation is Ross 614-B, its absolute
magnitude is 17, its luminosity is only 1/70,000th of the sun
and the mass is 1/12th of the mass of the sun.

[1] The letters B.D. stand for Argelander's Bonner Durchmusterung, the
"Bonn (stellar) Census."

CHAPTER XIV

NAMES IN THE SKY

THE STORY I HAVE IN MIND is probably being told in Los Angeles with the Griffith Observatory as its locale, in Chicago with reference to the Adler Planetarium and in any other city with reference to visitor's night at the nearby astronomical observatory. I heard it for the first time at the Treptow Observatory east of Berlin. It goes like this: the visitor looks through the telescope at the moon, then at Jupiter. Then two or three well-known stars are picked out to prove that a true star, even when seen through a telescope, still shows just as a pinpoint of light. The astronomer may say that Mars, unfortunately, can't be observed right now but will reappear in a a suitable location in the sky next November. And then the visitor says to another visitor: "I think I can understand how they measure the distance to Jupiter and how they find out how big it is. I can imagine how they make calculations telling them when a planet will be visible. What I don't understand is how they find out their *names!*"

If you change the joke to the serious question of how a name is established you not only have a legitimate question but you also have a problem. The answer is, of course, that somebody, at some time, gave a name to a star or to something more local, like a crater on the moon. But the names sometimes took hold and sometimes did not. There are even a few cases where everybody would be quite willing to go

along with the name favored by the discoverer, provided we could be sure that we know which astronomical object he had in mind. Conversely, with some star names of Arab origin we know which star is meant but we cannot interpret the name.

The names in the sky fall into two categories. The first is that of traditional names, where the name of the author is unknown. This category comprises the names of most of the constellations, the names of the naked-eye planets and the names of some of the more conspicuous stars. The second category is that of names which have been bestowed more recently—actually since the invention of the telescope in 1608 or 1609—by people who made astronomical discoveries. The names of the surface features of our moon, the names of a few planets and of all planetoids or asteroids and the names of moons of other planets make up the second category.

But even with these recent names some confusion is possible . . . and therefore exists.

Let us begin with the simplest case, the names of comets.

A good number of them have no "name" at all. The "Comet of 1577" has no name; it goes in astronomical literature under that designation. If comets do have names it is that of the discoverer; "Encke's Comet" has that name because it was discovered by Johann Franz Encke. And, to mention a recent example, "Comet Ikeya-Seki" is so named because two Japanese amateur astronomers with these names saw it first. In the case of "Biela's Comet" we really deal with the name of the re-discoverer, the Austrian army captain, Wilhelm von Biela. The comet had been seen earlier by Charles Messier in France, but it had been "lost" and Captain von Biela found it again. There is just one comet that is not named for its discoverer and that happens to be the most famous comet of

all: Halley's Comet. Dr. Edmond Halley, as a well-known but apparently anonymous ditty points out, did not discover his comet:

> The first to see it was not he
> But yet we call it Halley,
> The notion that it would return,
> Was his, origi-nally.

Halley had taken all the good comet observations he could find and tried to calculate their orbits. There was a total of about two dozen, and he soon saw that several of them followed very nearly the same orbit. And the times when these comets had been observed were always about 75 years apart. Thus Halley concluded that it was the same comet that had been seen in 1456, 1531, 1607 and 1682. On the last occasion he had seen it himself. He felt justified to predict another return for the year 1758. Halley died in 1742, and the first man to see the comet was a well-to-do and self-educated peasant by the name of Johann Georg Palitzsch. Nobody suggested that the comet should be named after Halley; the name grew more or less automatically out of statements like "the comet predicted by Dr. Halley."

While large naked-eye comets are comparatively rare, small comets, usually found photographically, are not. Several are found every year and a special system of designations has been introduced for them. At first these comets are listed as 1962a, 1962b, 1962c and so forth, in order of their discovery. Early in the following year the list is then rearranged to read 1962 I, 1962 II, 1962 III, etc., in order of their perihelion passages. Of course the name of the discoverer is attached too, and since one astronomer may discover more than one comet you might have a designation like Whipple IV, which means that it was the fourth comet discovered by Fred L. Whipple.

There is also a system for the naming of asteroids, the
planet fragments which normally orbit the sun between the
orbits of Mars and Jupiter. The first of them had been discovered during the New Year's Night 1800–1801 by Father
Giuseppe Piazzi, S.J. He first thought it was a comet; it
turned out to be a small planet in what up to that time had
been considered a "gap" in the solar system. In fact, some
two hundred years earlier Johannes Kepler had been so an-
noyed by the gap, which ruined his mathematical explanations,
that he wrote *Inter Jovem et Martem planetam interposui,*
"between Jupiter and Mars I put a planet." Now it had been
found by Piazzi and was named Ceres. As will be explained
later, astronomers had reasons to use names of the highest
classical purity.

The sequel to the story was that Ceres was lost for a while,
but the observed positions enabled Carl Friedrich Gauss to
calculate (by means of a new method which he invented for
the purpose) an ephemeris for the new planet. With the aid
of the position predicted by Gauss, Heinrich Wilhelm Olbers,
M.D., in Bremen, re-discovered Ceres. Soon after Olbers discovered another small planet in the same former gap which
was named Pallas. Two years later Karl Harding came up
with a third one, which was named Juno, and in 1807 Olbers
followed up with a fourth, to be named Vesta.

By then the pattern was established. Asteroids received classical female names.

This would have been most satisfactory as a system if there
had been not more than, say, five dozen asteroids. At first
Greek and Latin classical names were easy. Number 7 became Iris, number 27 was still Euterpe and number 57
Mnemosyne. But soon both Homer's *Odyssey* and Pliny's
Historia naturalis were exhausted. Oh, well, the Saga of Gudrun and the Nibelungenlied could be considered classical, too.

Names like Gudrun and Kriemhild began to invade the area populated by Leukothea and Klytemnaistra and Polyhymnia. Right now there is probably an actual need for female names, even though all common modern names in all languages, from Anna via Gertrud to Marlene and Natasha have been used. If a philologist would prove tomorrow that there was a Carthaginian goddess Ilu, her name would be attached to an asteroid the day after tomorrow.

There was some slight relief in 1898 when it was found that a newly discovered asteroid orbited partly inside the orbit of Mars. It was named Eros, a male name, to indicate that it differed from those in the by then very crowded "gap," and it quickly became customary to name all asteroids which crossed the orbits of either Mars or Jupiter, or orbited outside the orbit of Jupiter or inside the orbit of Mars, after males. In that sub-section of asteroid names all names are still strictly classical. There is a large supply of classical male names still available.

The names of the satellites of our solar system are now rather orderly but it wasn't always thus. Classical times, of course, knew only one satellite, that of Earth: Selene to the Greeks, Luna to the Romans. (The latter is the name for the moon in quite a number of modern languages, including Russian.) Our word moon is from the Anglo-Saxon *mona* (hence: month, in German *Monat*) and the other Germanic languages derive their names from the same root, e.g. *Maan* in Dutch and *Mond* in German. When Galileo Galilei discovered the four large moons of Jupiter two problems came up simultaneously. In the first place, since there was now not only the moon but *moons*, a general term for "moons" was desirable. Johannes Kepler supplied this by coining the word "satellite" (from *satellos*, which means attendant). But,

Galilei felt, the moons of Jupiter should also have individual names.

He wrote to Cosmo de Medici, Fourth Grand Duke of Tuscany, that they should be called the *Medicea Sidera*, the Medicean Stars, and suggested the specific names of members of the Medici family for them. To astronomers who were not Italians the name Medici simply did not have the exalted ring it had to Galilei and they kept silent on the proposal— except Herr Mayr in Kulmbach who called himself Simon Marius and who, being court astronomer to the Margrave of Brandenburg, suggested *Sidera Brandenburgica*. Marius, who claimed to have seen the moons of Jupiter earlier than Galilei —and who *did* discover the Great Nebula in Andromeda— realized after a discussion with Kepler that classical names were at least neutral, if not superior, and suggested naming the four major moons after four love affairs of Jove: Io, Europa, Ganymed and Callisto. With a long delay his suggestion was accepted even though, to this day, astronomers prefer to write J-I, J-II, J-III and J-IV. Galilei had started that by writing J., J.., J... and J::.

The system began to get into some trouble when E. E. Barnard, in 1892, discovered a fifth satellite of Jupiter which happened to orbit inside the four Galileian satellites. Barnard stuck to the designation J-V even though many names were proposed. Camille Flammarion in France suggested Amalthea (Jupiter's nursemaid in mythology) which is slowly coming into use, but usually with the parenthetical remark that it is "not official." (Because it was suggested by somebody other than the discoverer and not accepted by the discoverer.) Barnard's insistence on the designation J-V did have the result that the additional moons of Jupiter were not given any names but are referred to as J-VI, J-VII and so forth up to J-XII.

The outcome is that any list of Jupiter's satellites looks wrong. If you arrange it in the numerical order, which is the order of discovery, the satellites form no pattern as regard to distance from the planet. If you arrange them in order of distance from the planet, the numerals are out of sequence.

As for the moons of Saturn the confusion became such that finally names had to be called in. The first of them to be discovered, by Christiaan Huyghens in 1655, was Titan, but its discoverer simply called it *Luna Saturni*, Saturn's Moon. But then Giovanni Domenico Cassini discovered four more moons of Saturn. Collectively he wanted them to be known as the *Sydera Lodoicea* (the stars of Louis XIV) but individually he numbered them, in the order of distance from the planet. This made Huyghens' moon S-4. The end of discoveries, however, was not yet. William Herschel discovered two more, both closer to Saturn than the known ones. How to number now? Call them S-6 and S-7, as Herschel suggested (with S-7 being incongruously the closest to the planet) or should everything be re-numbered? And if that were done, who could guarantee that any additional discoveries would kindly orbit Saturn at a greater distance than those already numbered? It was Sir William Herschel's son, Sir John Herschel, who suggested to use the names of the mythological sisters and brothers of Saturn. This is the list—Mimas, Enceladus, Tethys, Dione, Rhea, Titan, Hyperion and Japetus—which is now generally used.

In 1898 Professor William H. Pickering added another moon and another sister of Saturn to the list: Phoebe.

Sir John Herschel also named the satellites of Uranus. His father had thought that he himself had discovered six satellites of Uranus. Four of them turned out to be mistakes, but two were real. William Lassell, in 1851, added two more so that four satellites were known. Sir John Herschel's proposed

names Ariel, Umbriel, Titania, and Oberon were accepted largely because Lassell, who had discovered two of them, accepted the names. (Oberon and Titania are, of course, the king and queen of the fairies in Shakespeare's *Midsummer Night's Dream*; Ariel is a spirit in *The Tempest* while Umbriel is a gnome and Ariel a sylph in Pope's *Rape of the Lock*.)

Still, it is interesting that a full dozen satellite names originated with a man who had not discovered a single one of them. When Gerard P. Kuiper discovered a fifth satellite of Uranus (closer to it than any of the others) he called it Miranda to stay within the mythology.

Neptune's major satellite was also discovered by William Lassell (in 1846) and Camille Flammarion suggested "Triton," Neptune's companion, as a name. Like Amalthea it is "not official" and for the same reason. But it is in use now, largely because Kuiper, when discovering a second satellite of Neptune in 1949, named it "Nereid" which he, as the discoverer, had the right to do.

The two moons of Mars, discovered by Asaph Hall in 1877, are, of course, Phobos and Deimos (Fear and Terror), the attendants of Mars in the ninth book of the *Iliad*.

The names of the five naked-eye planets are fairly easy. Still, it may be useful to mention first that the word "planet" comes from the Greek *planetes* (the wanderers) because they do not stand still in the sky like the "fixed" stars. The word "comet," incidentally, comes from the Latin word *coma* ("head of hair").

Now Mercury, the innermost of the planets, is the fastest moving, in reality as well as to the naked eye. Hence it became, in Greek, Hermes (properly Hermeias) the swift-moving messenger of the gods. The Latin name Mercurius also bears the connotation of swift movement but is derived from *mercis*, which means "wares." Hence Mercurius became the

god of the traders and merchants but also the god of the thieves—for which latter fact one may harbor two different opinions; one is unflattering to merchants, the other merely points out that a thief has to move even faster than a trader. The names for Mercury in the eastern languages usually are the word for "arrow," or a name derived from that word.

Venus, bright and beautiful, became female with all nations except in India. The Chinese called Venus *Tai-pe*, "the beautiful white one." To the Germanic tribes the planet was Frigga; to the Babylonians Ishtar; to the Romans Venus. Venus was originally the Spring Goddess and only later the goddess of love, equivalent to the Greek Aphrodite. Since Venus can appear either as morning or as evening star, the Greeks originally had two names for the planet, Hesperos and Phosphoros. Pythagoras of Samos is credited with having identified them as the same planet.

As unanimously as white Venus became a beautiful woman, red Mars became a warrior. The Persians called Mars Pahlavani Siphir, the Celestial Warrior. To the Chaldeans he was Nergal, the god of battle, to the Greeks Ares, also the god of war, regardless of whether the name is derived from *áro* (to kill) or from *árá* (disaster). The Germans also identified the planet with their god of war, and Roman Mars is, of course, the god of war too.

As for Jupiter it probably was given the name of the chief deity of the Romans—the name is stated to be derived from *Iovis pater*—because of its steady light, being the brightest of the planets except Venus. Of course Jupiter is the equivalent of Zeus. And it is also quite possible that the naming went the other way round, that the god was given the name of the serenely shining planet, for when you said in Latin *sub Iove* it meant "under the open sky."

Saturn, in Latin Saturnus, was, mythologically speaking, the

god of agriculture and the husband of Ops, the goddess of wealth. The name is related to the verb *serere*, "to sow." The Greek equivalent was Kronos. Why the name of the god of agriculture was bestowed upon the planet is something that I would have considered a mystery until about three months ago, when I found an interesting reference in a recent book on the planet Saturn by the British astronomer A. F. O'D. Alexander. He states that the name most often used for Saturn by the Assyrians was *lubadsagush* which, since *lubad* meant "old sheep," has to be translated as "the oldest of the old sheep," another agricultural comparison. Alexander thinks that the name was due to the fact that Saturn moves so slowly among the stars. Possibly Saturn's slow movement accounts for its Latin name too, reminding the skywatchers of the slow gait of ploughing oxen.

For the remaining three planets there is no mystery about their names. When William Herschel discovered Uranus he first proposed the name of *Georgium Sidus* in honor of George III. Outside of Great Britain nobody was pleased with this suggestion, which revived what Galilei and then Cassini had tried to do. Joseph Jérôme Lalande in Paris suggested that the newly discovered planet should be known as Herschel's Planet, in the same manner in which one speaks of Halley's Comet.

But there was no enthusiasm for this innovation. Other astronomers felt that it was enough to be able to attach one's name to a comet (or to have a lunar crater named after one —posthumously, that is) and when Johann Elert Bode, the director of the Berlin observatory, suggested Uranus most astronomers agreed rapidly. It was actually the offshoot of the Herschel-Lalande-Bode controversy which produced the severely classical names for the first asteroids some dozen years later. The word Uranus is just the Latin version of the Greek Ouranos which means heaven or sky.

The pattern repeated sixty-five years later when Galle in Berlin discovered Neptune close to the point where Leverrier in Paris had said it should be located. Leverrier had calculated its existence and position from the perturbations of the orbit of Uranus. The French scientist François Arago—who had a political in addition to a scientific career and was, among other things, responsible for the abolition of slavery in the French colonies—revived the suggestion to name Uranus "Herschel's Planet" so that the new one could become "Leverrier's Planet." It did not go very far, for the French *Bureau des Longitudes* decided that Neptune was a fine name for a far distant greenish planet and Leverrier himself agreed. The name Neptunus is that of the Latin god of the seas, equivalent to the Greek Poseidon, but neither Romans nor classical Greeks ever had an opportunity to attach it to a planet

Pluto, discovered by Clyde Tombaugh in 1930, was named for what might be called a personal reason. Just as Leverrier, and also John Couch Adams in England, had calculated Neptune's existence from irregularities in the motions of Uranus, Percival Lowell had tried to calculate the existence and position of one more planet from the same source. He had called it Planet X but after the discovery of a planet which is (for about two thirds of its orbit) farther from the sun than Neptune, it became obvious that that name could not be used permanently. But the discovery had been made at Lowell's observatory, though long after his death, and since the name Pluto begins with P-L it was chosen. It was correct mythologically too, for Pluto, the lord of the infernal region, was a brother of both Zeus (Jupiter) and Poseidon (Neptune).

Before going on to the names of stars the names of two sets of features must be mentioned. It has already been said that an astronomer's name might be selected posthumously for a crater on the moon. Two people are responsible for

this custom: Langrenus of Brussels and Riccioli of Bologna. Langrenus made the suggestion of naming lunar features after famous people, especially astronomers, around 1640. Johannes Hevelius of Danzig, five years later, opposed it and transferred terrestrial geographical names to the moon, which is the reason why we speak of the Lunar Alps, the Lunar Caucasus, etc. But Giovanni Batista Riccioli, five years after Hevelius's lunar map with terrestrial names, accepted Langrenus's suggestion. He even had a kind of a system. He named a large crater Plato, then attached the names of Eudoxus, Aristotle, Thales, Strabo, etc., to craters not far from Plato. Riccioli admired Tycho Brahe; therefore the most conspicuous crater was named Tycho. Since Copernicus did not agree with Tycho Brahe, the lunar crater Copernicus is far away from the crater Tycho. But since Kepler agreed with Copernicus, the crater Kepler is near the crater Copernicus.

The visible features of the planet Mars went through a number of linguistic transformations. It was only just about a century ago that telescopes became powerful enough to show surface features on Mars and, logically, observers in different countries began making drawings of Mars. And they started naming things, in their own tongues. Thus a map of Mars drawn by Richard Anthony Proctor in 1867, following Riccioli's practice, is full of names of astronomers. There is a Herschel I Continent, a Herschel II Strait, Fontana Land, Laplace Land, Tycho Sea and so forth, all in English, of course. On a map drawn by Camille Flammarion some of the names are the same, like the Herschel I Continent, but others are changed. What Proctor had called the Kaiser Sea (after the Dutch astronomer Kaiser) appeared on Flammarion's map as *Mer du Sablier*. What Proctor had called Dawes Continent (after the Rev. William Dawes) became the

NAMES IN THE SKY **193**

Continent Beer (after the German Beer, the brother of the composer Meyerbeer). What Proctor had named Maedler Land, after a German astronomer, became, on Flammarion's map *Terre de Laplace*; he named something else after Maedler. Of course, the whole map was in French.

Well, the third to draw a map was Giovanni Virginio Schiaparelli in Italy. What Flammarion had called *Mer Terby* appeared on Schiaparelli's map as *Solis Lacus*; what had been the Kaiser Sea or the *Mer du Sablier*, respectively, appeared as *Syrtis Major*. The light area around Lacus Solis, *Terre de Kepler* on Flammarion's map, became *Thaumasia*. The *Mer de Fontana* became *Elysium* and the *Mer Oudemans* became *Trivium Charontis*. By the grace of God Schiaparelli's system won out in all countries, and most of his names are still in use. By being Latin they are the same in all languages, because they are nobody's language.

We now come to the names of constellations and of some conspicuous stars, but for practical reasons the evolution of the current system has to be discussed first.

Hipparch's star catalogue, as preserved for us in the Almagest, listed a total of 1022 stars which, of course, are all naked-eye stars, leaving out a number of faint ones and, naturally, neglecting the southern hemisphere almost completely. (At a later date the Belgian astronomer, Jean Charles Houzeau stated that a man with perfect vision, if he first counted from a rather northern latitude and then continued from a southern latitude, would reach a total of 5719 stars.) Now all stars were sorted into six classes according to their apparent brightness. The brightest ones were in the first class (later called the first magnitude) and the just visible ones formed the sixth class.

So far there was no special problem, but this soon ceased to be the case if a specific star was to be picked out. The

invention of the constellations helped. A total of forty-eight are listed in the Almagest: the twelve signs of the zodiac, twenty-one constellations north of the zodiac and fifteen to the south of the zodiac. (The names of almost all of them are still in use.) A constellation was useful for stating which star one had in mind, in that it limited the area of the sky. In fact, this is the main reason why the names of constellations are still used, and at the Astronomical Congress at Leyden (The Netherlands) in 1928 the limits of the constellations were carefully established. Modern star charts have the eighty-eight constellations agreed upon during that congress.

But to go back to the Greek astronomers. The star Hipparch had in mind (Aldebaran) was in the constellation *Taurus* and had to be described as "the bright star in the southern eye of the bull." Or another star (Rigel) had to be designated as "the bright star in Orion's left foot."

One wonders why the Greeks did not think of the simple device of just numbering the stars in a constellation after they had once been carefully described in the elaborate manner just quoted. But they didn't.

Alessandro Piccolomini, in 1568, took the first step in that direction. He omitted the usually rather elaborate mythological pictures, also all the faint stars, but he gave a map showing the positions of the larger stars and labeled them with the Latin alphabet. A German lawyer who was an ardent astronomer, Johannes Bayer, did what we do now. He labeled the stars in each constellation with Greek letters, switching to the Latin alphabet only when there were more stars in a constellation than the Greek alphabet has letters. In his book, the *Uranometria*, which appeared for the first time in 1603, he said that it was his system to call the brightest star of each constellation *alpha*, the next brightest *beta*, the third brightest *gamma*, the fourth *delta* and so on. Of course, he made a

number of mistakes. His *alpha* is not always the brightest star; but that his idea was good is proved by the simple fact that we still use it. Thus we say that the first photographs of Pluto were found on a plate centered on *delta Geminorum*, the fourth brightest star in the constellation Gemini. Bayer's system is such a space-saving device; Aldebaran becomes *alpha Tauri*, Capella *alpha Aurigae*, Castor and Pollux *alpha* and *beta Geminorum* and Sirius *alpha Canis majoris*. In the course of time stars at the border of one constellation have often been shifted into the neighboring constellation, sometimes deliberately, more often by mistake. Even the famous zodiac did not remain unaffected. The Greeks had only eleven zodiacal signs for several centuries. *Libra*, in that zodiac, had turned into the pincers of the neighboring constellation *Scorpio*. Tracing the shifts of this type is a whole sub-branch of the history of astronomy which has the special name of Astrognosis. This is the area where astronomy and archeology (plus "ordinary history") touch and overlap.

Many of the individual names of stars are Arabic but they are not always "pure." In addition to truly old Arabic names there are many which are pseudo-Arabic, being Arabic adaptations of names from other languages. And later on many of them went through another transformation, usually Latinization, to make them pronounceable for European tongues. Aldebaran is a case in point. The Arabic form *addabaran* was produced by translating a Greek sentence. An expert on Arabic astronomy, Dr. Paul Kunitzsch, a German living in Cairo, says that Arab scholars themselves are uncertain what the word really means but think the root word is *dbr* which means "to be behind something" or "to follow something." The meaning, astrognostically speaking, would then be "the star which follows the Hyades."

What name could sound more "Arabic" than Algol? Well,

it is Arabic all right, but not originally so. The star Algol, *beta Persei* on charts, was the Gorgon's head. This designation, in Arabic, became *ra's al-gul*, the head of the Gul, a demon in Arabic mythology. As for Deneb, *alpha Cygni* the current name is an abbreviation. The Arabic original is *danab ad-dagaga*, "tail of the chicken."

I have mentioned earlier that the star *beta Orionis* was described by the Greeks as the "bright star in Orion's left foot." The Arabic version was *rigl al-yusra*, "Orion's foot," and the star is called Rigel to this day—though nobody is quite certain how it should be pronounced.

While it is interesting to find out why a number of bright stars bears the names they do, individual star names are slowly coming out of use. Which, considering everything, is probably a logical development. As distinct from the names of the constellations, which are useful as area designations, there is little need for individual star names.

Except for the few Arabic-sounding star names just discussed we have dealt mainly with modern names so far. Progressing to the constellations, we'll mainly deal with traditional names. Let us begin with the Zodiac, the twelve constellations which lie in the outward projection of the plane of the earth's orbit, hence the constellations entered by the sun in the course of one year.

Most of the names of the signs of the Zodiac do not need any explanation. They are, in their customary order and in the Latin version, the following:

Aries (the Ram), *Taurus* (the Bull) and *Gemini* (the Twins, named "Castor and Pollux" in the Greek version and "Man and Wife" in sixteenth-century Europe), followed by *Cancer* (the Crab, or the Crayfish in western Europe), *Leo* (the Lion) and *Virgo*, (the Virgin, originally just "the

Woman"). The next constellation, *Libra* (the Scales) is the one Ptolemy made a separate constellation. Before him the Greeks had considered the constellation *Libra* to be a part, namely the pincers, of the following constellation *Scorpio* while the Romans considered it the scales held by Themis, which was the same as the preceding constellation *Virgo*. Though Ptolemy gave it the rank of a separate constellation he still called it *chelai*, "the pincers." The constellations following *Libra*, are, of course, *Scorpius* (the Scorpion), *Sagittarius* (the Archer), *Capricornus* (the Goat, originally the Fish-Goat) *Aquarius* (the Water Carrier) and *Pisces* (the Fishes).

It may be necessary to mention that the word "Zodiac" itself is derived from the Greek word *zoon* which means "animal." Most of the signs are animals and some that are not now animals were animals in the past; *Sagittarius*, the archer, was originally a centaur. It is interesting that the Zodiac of other civilizations is completely a "circle of animals," as the following tabulation, borrowed from Dr. Huberta von Bronsart, shows.

Zodiac	Chinese (and Japanese)	Siamese	Persian	Egyptian
Ram	Dog	Dog	Dog	Tomcat
Bull	Rooster	Rooster	Hen	Dog
Twins	Monkey	Monkey	Monkey	Serpent
Crab	Sheep	Goat	Sheep	Scarab
Lion	Horse	Horse	Horse	Ass
Virgin	Snake	Small Dragon	Snake	Lion
Scales	Dragon	Large Dragon	Crocodile	Billy goat
Scorpion	Hare	Rabbit	Hare	Bull
Archer	Tiger	Tiger	Tiger	Falcon
Goat	Bull	Cow	Ox	Monkey
Water Carrier	Rat	Rat	Mouse	Ibis
Fishes	Pig	Pig	Pig	Crocodile

The 21 constellations of the Almagest to the north of the Zodiac begin with *Ursa minor* as the first and *Ursa major* as the second. That the Little Dipper, to use the American name, came ahead of the Big Dipper was due to the fact that it contains the pole star. The words mean, of course, Little Bear and Great Bear; originally the four stars of the Great Bear that form a quadrangle were the "she-bear" and the three stars of the handle were three bear cubs trailing her. Great Wain and Lesser Wain were alternate names of the same two constellations. Then followed:

No. 3. *Draco* (the Dragon)

No. 4. *Cepheus* (this is a personal name, presumed to be the Latin version of the name of an Ethiopian king)

No. 5. *Boötes* (the Driver of the Oxen, or the Custodian of the Bears)

No. 6. *Corona borealis* (the Northern Crown)

No. 7. *Hercules* (in Ptolemy's Almagest, "the Kneeling man")

No. 8. *Lyra* (originally a turtle, the shell of which Hermes used for making a lyre, a rather poetic development)

No. 9. *Cygnus* (the Swan; in Ptolemy "the Bird")

No. 10. *Cassiopeia* (wife of Cepheus; on some old charts this constellation is called the Throne or the Queen's Throne)

No. 11. *Perseus* (the rescuer of Andromeda)

No. 12. *Auriga* (the Drayman)

No. 13. *Ophiuchus* (the Carrier of the Serpent)

No. 14. *Serpens* (the serpent carried by Ophiuchus)

No. 15. *Sagitta* (the Arrow)

No. 16. *Aquila* (the Eagle)

No. 17. *Delphinus* (the Dolphin)

No. 18. *Equuleus* (the Filly; in Ptolemy the "Front Part of the Horse")

No. 19. *Pegasus* (the Horse; not a winged horse in Ptolemy)

No. 20. *Andromeda* (the daughter of Cepheus and Cassio-peia)

No. 21. *Triangulum* (the Triangle; originally the Nile Delta)

The constellations to the south of the Zodiac were:

No. 34. *Cetus* (the Whale)

No. 35. *Orion* (the Hunter)

No. 36. *Eridanus* (the River; in Ptolemy this constellation is called *potamos* which is the Greek word for river, meaning the Nile. The Romans changed this to Eridanus, the Amber River, which was their name for the Elbe river in Germany; later they called the same river Albis—which caused a lot of confusion)

No. 37. *Lepus* (the Hare)

No. 38. *Canis major* (the Big Dog; in Ptolemy just *Kynos*, the dog)

No. 39. *Canis minor* (the Little Dog; in Ptolemy this constellation was called *prokyon*, which is now the name of its principal star)

No. 40. *Argo navis* (the Ship; since it also served as the symbol of the year it was pictured with either 12 or 52 oars, symbolizing months or weeks)

No. 41. *Hydra* (the Sea Serpent)

No. 42. *Crater* (the Cup)

No. 43. *Corvus* (the Raven)

No. 44. *Centaurus* (the Centaur)

No. 45. *Lupus* (the Wolf. In Ptolemy this constellation is just *therion*, which means "wild beast"; the Arabs were the ones who substituted a specific wild beast)

No. 46. *Ara* (the Altar)

No. 47. *Corona australis* (the Southern Crown; the Arabs called it the Ostrich Nest)

No. 48. *Piscis austrinus* (the Southern Fish)

The constellation now known as *Coma Berenices* (the Hair of Berenice) was suggested before Ptolemy by the Greek astronomer Hipparchos, but for unknown reasons were not accepted by Ptolemy.

During the sixteenth and seventeenth centuries three more constellations were added: *Monoceros* (the Unicorn), *Camelopardalis* (the Giraffe) and *Columba* (the Dove). The latter is credited in countless books to Dr. Edmond Halley but it was actually suggested by the Dutch geographer Pieter Plancius. The gradual mapping of the southern sky which followed in the wake of geographical exploration added literally dozens of new constellations, most of which were dropped later. It may be mentioned at this point that the early explorers expected the southern sky to be a replica (or else a mirror image) of the northern sky and they were puzzled that this did not turn out to be the case. They were especially disappointed that there was no South Pole Star.

This disappointment did not prevent them from making charts of the southern sky and the first set of new (southern) constellations was published by Bayer in his *Uranometria*, the book that introduced the Greek letter designations for the brighter stars. The new names were designed to sound tropical, they were *Chameleon, Dorado* (Goldfish, sometimes mistranslated as swordfish), *Phoenix, Indus* (the Indian), *Pavo* (the Peacock), *Grus* (the Crane; but it was the flamingo that Bayer had in mind—unfortunately his artist had never seen one), *Hydrus* (the Water Snake), *Tucana* (the Toucan), *Columba* (the Dove), *Musca* (the Fly), *Crux* (the Southern Cross), and *Apus* (the footless).

The last two need a few words of explanation. Alvise de Cadamosto, in 1454, had called the Southern Cross the Southern Wain, he was one of those who expected the southern

sky to be the equivalent of the northern sky. Amerigo Ves-
pucci had named it *Rhombus*. The first man to call it a
cross was Andrea Corsali in 1515. As for *Apus* the word means
"footless" and a few modern authors, to whom this made
no sense, decided that the name was a misprint and "cor-
rected" it to *Apis* (the Bee). The correct translation is Bird
of Paradise, for in 1600 it was believed that the Bird of
Paradise never alighted on the ground and was, for that reason, footless.

The next set of constellations appeared in the *Prodromus
Astronomiae* of Johannes Hevelius. Hevelius, whose real
name was Hewelcke, had been improving on this book all
his life so that it was not printed until 1690, three years
after the author's death. It introduced *Lacerta* (the Lizard)[1],
Leo minor (the Little Lion), *Canes venatici* (the Hunting
Dogs), *Sextans* (the Sextant), *Scutum* (the Shield or Buckler;
Hevelius called it *Scutum Sobiesii*, the Shield of Sobieski,
in honor of the king of Poland) and *Vulpecula*. The last
is usually called the Fox in English though the word means
Little Fox. The original name was *Vulpecula cum ansere*,
the Little Fox and the Goose. Finally Hevelius, needing a
constellation to fill in space in an area where there were only
very faint stars, created the constellation *Lynx*, with the
statement that one had to have the eyes of a lynx to see
anything at all in that area.

The final set of names of constellations of the southern sky
originated with the abbé Nicolas Louis de Lacaille, who
had carried out a careful mapping operation from the Cape of
Good Hope during the years from 1751 to 1754. Lacaille decided on modern terms and things, just to indicate that these

---

[1] *Lacerta* replaced the "Hand of Justice" (of Louis XIV) of a French
globe of the sky. On the same globe *Musca* was represented by the *fleur-de-
lis*.

constellations and their stars had not been known to the ancients. His constellations are:

Antlia (originally *Antlia pneumatica,* the Air Pump)
Caelum (originally *Caelum sculptoris,* the Sculptor's Tool)
Circinus (the Compasses, originally *Circinus et norma,* Compasses and Ruler)
Fornax (the Furnace)
Horologium (the Pendulum Clock)
Mensa (the Table, originally *Mons mensae,* the Table Mountain, meaning Table Mountain near Cape Town in South Africa, from which Nicolas Louis de Lacaille, who introduced this constellation, observed the southern sky)
Microscopium (the Microscope)
Norma (the Ruler, but in the sense of "straightedge")
Pictor (originally *Equus pictoris,* the Painter's Easel)
Pyxis (the Mariner's Compass. The literal meaning of the word is "small (wooden) box"; it came to mean Mariner's Compass via the Italian form, *bussola della calamita,* which was a wooden bowl, filled with water, in which a reed (*calamita*), supporting the magnetic needle was floating)
Reticulum (the Net; actually Lacaille's *reticule romboide,* the instrument he used for measuring angular distances between the stars) and finally
Sculptor and *Telescopium.*

Of course, many more names for constellations have been proposed by various astronomers at various times, for example Father Maximilian Hell, S.J., of Vienna suggested to take the stars in the area where Herschel had discovered Uranus and make a constellation to be named *Tubus major Herschelii* (Herschel's Large Telescope) and another one, *Tubus minor Herschelii* (Herschel's Small Telescope), in the area

where the planetary nature of Uranus was verified. I have mentioned only those constellations that are now "official" and listed in Delporte's *Atlas Celeste*.

But even for this atlas one more innovation was needed, the old and unwieldy constellation No. 40, *Argo*, was divided into three, named *Carina*, *Vela* and *Puppis* (Keel, Sails and Poop), but the Greek letters for the stars in these constellations form one sequence through all three.

CHAPTER XV

COLLECTOR'S MISCELLANY

1. *The Secrets of Enoch*

JUST ABOUT THE TIME when the nature of the Podkamennaya Tunguska meteorite (see Chapter XII) was hotly debated in Russia, another mysterious remark passed through the iron curtain. The international scientific journal *Planetary and Space Science*, in its May 1963 issue, carried an article by a Russian scientist who said, in passing, that he did not agree with the suggestion made by some Russian writers that a passage in *The Book of the Secrets of Enoch* contained a reference to the landing of extraterrestrial visitors on earth.

Having never even heard of a *Book of Enoch*, I embarked on the customary journey to the New York Public Library on Fifth Avenue and Forty-second Street for enlightenment. Fortunately the *Book of Enoch* was in the card index; it had been translated into English in 1896 by William Richard Morfill of Oxford University. It is one of a set of ancient books that go under the collective designation of "apocalyptic writings."

The Enoch to whom it is attributed is the Enoch of *Genesis* V:18–24, the father of Methuselah and great grandfather of Noah. There are, as I learned from Mr. Morfill, two books of Enoch, one in Ethiopian and one in Slavonic but, again according to Mr. Morfill, they have nothing in common

but the title. The Slavonic version is known in several copies, the most recent of which is a part of a *Sbornik* (collection) of the seventeenth century.

The book must have been written at about the time of Christ, for it is quoted in the so-called Epistle of Barnabas which is dated somewhere between 70 and 90 A.D. and in a few writings which are a few years older than Barnabas. But the writer was evidently somebody who spoke Greek and in all probability, Greek only because he told why Adam was given his name. According to this book the Lord wanted to indicate that Adam and his seed were to rule the earth, hence he was named after the four quarters of the earth which are: *anatole* (sunrise or east), *dysis* (sunset or west), *arktos* (north) and *mesembria* (south), hence a-d-a-m! That this little anagram works in Greek only and not in any other language did not occur to the writer.

The contents of the book are that Enoch is shown the heavens and that the Lord then decrees that Enoch shall be permitted to hear the sacred books. He is taken aside by the archangel Vretil (Morfill remarks that this name does not occur anywhere else; my Greek dictionary supplies the information that *bretas* is the term for a wooden image of a god; this may or may not be the root word) who reads to him for thirty days and nights without stopping, Enoch taking down every word. Then he is returned to earth.

All the time I was, of course, waiting for the passage which Russian writers, to whom the *Book of Enoch* is obviously more familiar than to us, had interpreted as being a record of an extraterrestrial visit. Finally, near the very end, I found the only lines which could conceivably be meant:

"LXVII (1) When Enoch has discoursed with the people, the Lord sent a darkness upon the earth, and there was a

gloom, and it had those men standing with Enoch. (2) And the angel hasted and took Enoch and carried him to the highest heaven where the Lord secured him, and set him before his face, and the darkness departed from the earth and there was light. (3) And the people saw and did not understand how Enoch was taken, and they glorified God. And they who had seen such things departed to their houses."

Since the whole work is one of religious imagery, the statement that Enoch was carried to the highest heaven while a supernatural darkness surrounded him can hardly be interpreted as having a physical meaning.

As a matter of fact the whole last scene is just an elaboration of *Genesis* V:24 "And Enoch walked with God; and he *was* not; for God took him." And it is probably this line which caused the ancient Greek-speaking writer to single him out as the central character of his own work. Most of the other people mentioned in *Genesis* simply die.

2. The Original Inventor of Recording Tape

BACK IN 1957 when Project Vanguard was discussed in the newspapers, at least once every week a columnist who should have stuck to her normal subject declared that "all this has been made possible through the recent wonderful discovery of making oxygen a liquid."

For a few minutes I toyed with the idea of just how to phrase a sarcastic letter pointing out that the discovery of liquefying oxygen was older than the columnist unless I estimated her age in a manner unbecoming to a gentleman. But while phrasing this letter (which was never written) I suddenly realized that some of the other things that go into the making of a large liquid fuel rocket were equally old, for example centrifugal pumps, pressure bottles for holding gas with which to run gyroscopes and the gyroscopes themselves. I had little trouble in drawing up a list of the items that are needed, each one accompanied by the date of invention (or discovery) and found that a liquid fuel rocket with a vertical range of about 100 miles could have been built in 1906—certainly in 1910—if the proper synthesis of the existing pieces of knowledge and of hardware had been made then.

A number of years later I repeated the story during a lecture to an engineering society in the Los Angeles area

and during the social hour that followed the lecture more than one engineer, engaged in space work, let out thoughtful moans which could be vocalized as: "What do we have now that could be put together for something revolutionary if only somebody had the necessary vision for a synthesis?"

I regret sincerely that I cannot answer this question—if I could I'd get myself a few patents and tell industry to negotiate with my attorney. But I can tell a story that illustrates the opposite case, that of a man who had vision and the right idea but who could not do anything with it because a needed invention or two had not yet been made. His name was Oberlin Smith and he should be regarded as the original inventor of recording tape, useful from kindergarten to orbiting satellites.

The original publication by Oberlin Smith took place in the long defunct journal *The Electrical World*, issue of September 8, 1888. His opening paragraph read: "There being nowadays throughout the scientific world great activity of thought regarding listening and talking machines (both Alexander Graham Bell and Thomas Alva Edison had obtained their patents for the telephone and for the phonograph about a decade earlier, in 1877) the readers of *The Electrical World* may be interested in a description of two or three possible methods of making a phonograph which the writer contrived some years ago, but which were laid aside and never brought to completion on account of a press of other work."

The first of Smith's suggestions was a possible improvement of Edison's phonograph by inscribing the sound not on tinfoil (as Edison did) but on a "thin ribbon of iron, steel or other substance capable of being temporarily softened by heat." The ribbon was to have a width of about $1/30^{th}$ of an inch and a probable thickness of $1/200^{th}$ of an inch. The idea was to soften the ribbon by a heat lamp just before

it reached the inscribing needle and to have the distance between recording needle and receiving reel long enough so that the ribbon would be hard again when wound on the reel. Looking back at this suggestion from the vantage point provided by the three quarters of a century that have passed, one can say that this probably would not have worked out well with a metallic ribbon but that Mr. Smith might have been quite successful if thermo-setting plastics (or even ordinary thermoplastics) had existed in his time.

But it is the next suggestion that makes Oberlin Smith the original inventor of the recording tape. He proceeded to point out that an "all-electric method" is likely to be superior to a mechanical method. He wanted to pass a "cord" through a coil connected with a microphone so that "the cord becomes, so to speak, a series of short magnets grouped into alternate swellings and attenuations of magnetism."

"The cord," he continued, "therefore contains a perfect record of the sound, far more delicate than the indentations in the tinfoil of the mechanical phonograph. The probable construction of the cord would be a cotton, silk or other thread, among whose fibres would be spun (or otherwise mixed) hard steel dust, or short clippings of very fine steel wire, hardened. Each piece would, of course, become a complete magnet. Other forms of the cord might be a brass, lead or other wire or ribbon through which the steel dust was mixed in melting, being hardened afterwards in the case of brass or any metal with a high melting point. Another (but too expensive), form would be a chain with each link a magnet; or, if the magnets affected each other too much when in contact, each alternate link could be of non-magnetic material."

Oberlin Smith did not think that the idea of a chain, already discarded because of its probable high price, was as

good as the idea of dust magnets imbedded in a thread or ribbon of non-metallic material. And he mentioned, but discarded, the idea that it might be possible to use just a steel wire, because he doubted that the steel wire "would divide itself up properly into a number of short magnets. The magnetic influence would be distributed along the wire in a most totally depraved way, with nodal points just where they were not wanted."

The reason why Smith did not follow up on his own ideas was not just the "press of other work" as he had cited in the beginning. He had run into too many practical difficulties. He had developed a machine for spinning dust into a cotton thread, but had been unable to harden steel dust because of oxidation taking place in the process. He had chopped up steel wire and found that a piece of wire had to be three or four times as long as its diameter, or else the small pieces would not become magnets, at least in his own experiments. He had tried to find information on very small magnets in contemporary books, but such information either did not exist, or else it had not been published in English. He had approached other researchers with his problem, admitting his ignorance, but "had found an equal amount of ignorance in several well-known electricians."

Again, from the vantage point of three quarters of a century later, it is easy to see what went wrong. Oberlin Smith had what he considered to be an interesting and possibly workable idea. But it was far more than that, it was a project that would require an extensive research program of several thousand scientific man hours. Realizing this to some extent, he had decided to publish his ideas, "hoping that some of the numerous experimenters now working in this field may find a germ of good from which something useful may grow."

The other experimenters did not pay any known attention to Smith's "germ," either because they realized the magnitude of the job to be done or—more probable—because they were busy with projects of their own.

The first man who actually built a recording device along the lines suggested by Smith was the Danish inventor Valdemar Poulson who probably never saw Smith's article. One of the reasons for saying so is that Poulson did use a steel wire. His instrument was called the "Telegraphon" and it was one of the many attractions of the Paris Exposition of 1900. Among the important men of the time who listened to the inventor's explanation was old Emperor Franz Josef of Austria who then said into the microphone: "This new invention is most interesting to me and I thank you very much for its demonstration,"—and then listened to his own voice. In all probability Franz Josef was as surprised at the sound of his own voice as everybody else who hears it for the first time. But in spite of its public success at the Exposition the "Telegraphon" remained a one-time attempt, possibly because the phonograph was reasonably well established.

Well, where and when did the recording tape of today begin? It began with the German patent No. 500,900, granted to one Fritz Pfleumer of Dresden in 1928 who claimed the invention of recording sound on paper ticker tape that had been covered with iron dust. He actually built an apparatus for demonstration, but the first results were hardly acceptable. He offered his invention, among others, to the A.E.G. (*Allgemeine Electricitäts-Gesellschaft*), the German counterpart of General Electric. The research chiefs of the A.E.G. reacted precisely as Oberlin Smith had hoped his contemporaries would react. They decided that this was

a useful idea, but totally useless without lots of developmental work.

One of the things that Mr. Pfleumer's tape did was to produce cracking noises at random intervals. They were finally traced to almost microscopic holes in the paper tape. Paper manufacturers had never been asked to produce thin paper that did not have microscopic holes and when confronted with such a request said two things: (1) that thin paper apparently was bound to have such holes and that there was nothing they could do about it; (2) if the elimination of such holes was so important, why didn't A.E.G. glue two tapes together? Each tape would have holes, but that the holes would match was most unlikely.

Of course that was correct, but paper tape just was not strong enough and A.E.G. threw the project into the lap of a chemical plant in Ludwigshafen: "Find something that behaves like paper in every physical aspect but is stronger and, if possible, fireproof." That was the request. The chemists of the company felt that the final request—namely that the tape should be fireproof—was unreasonable. They ignored it and, in 1932, began to experiment with tapes of cellulose acetate. Two years later they had something that could be publicly demonstrated, the occasion was a Radio Exposition in Berlin in 1934. By 1939 the factory produced over 16 million feet of recording tape.

Ten years after the first public demonstration a new material was found, namely polyvinylchloride. And that was the recording tape we now know, based on a principle Oberlin Smith had thought up back in 1888.

3. *The Accident that Didn't Happen*

A FEW YEARS AGO I bought a very interesting document, interesting for more than one reason. In physical shape it is a typescript of an article, only three and a half pages long, written about 1910. It must have been printed in some journal or magazine, for on the first page there are some penciled notes about type size to be used and so forth. But I don't know where it was published, nor do I know how the manuscript found its way to the antiquarian from whom I bought it. The last page bears the author's signature: Hudson Maxim.

Before I go on, I had better explain just who Hudson Maxim was. The mention of the name of Maxim brings to mind the Maxim gun, but its inventor was Sir Hiram Stevens Maxim, who died in 1916. If the name made you think of the Maxim silencer, you were one generation closer to the present, for the silencer was invented by Sir Hiram's son, Hiram Percy Maxim, who died in 1936. The Hudson Maxim who wrote the article I am going to discuss was Sir Hiram's younger brother (died in 1927) who founded the Columbia Powder Company and then the Maxim Powder Company—finally sold to E. I. Dupont de Nemours—and invented the explosive called maximite.

Having the "who's who" straightened out, we can proceed to the piece itself. It opens with the following sentence: "The enormous energy developed by the combustion of high explosives and smokeless powders has led many to conclude that such materials could be utilized to advantage in some form of internal combustion engine especially designed for the purpose."

This sounds like a fairly innocuous beginning, and when I read it, I felt sure what the argument in the next paragraph would be. To my surprise, the argument I expected was not developed. Hudson Maxim, a few lines later, pointed out that a "smokeless powder combines within itself both the fuel and the oxygen for its own combustion; hence, it is a fuel in which the combustible is chemically combined with oxygen, and is consequently a much more expensive fuel than gasoline or anything now used in internal combustion engines." The line of reasoning is this: "The oxygen contained in an explosive cannot be compared in cheapness with atmospheric oxygen, which does not cost anything."

All true, of course, but I would have expected that one of the foremost authorities on high explosives would have pointed out something different. The main argument is that a smokeless powder or a high explosive does *not* contain more energy than ordinary engine fuels. Most likely this simply had not yet been measured in 1910, strange as it may seem in retrospect.

For a good comparison of the energy content of various fuels, the exhaust velocity (theoretical) when used in a rocket is a fine yardstick. Now if you compare these theoretical exhaust velocities, you get the following somewhat unexpected list:

Dynamite (if it could be used in a rocket motor) has a theoretical exhaust velocity of almost precisely 11,000 feet

per second. Smokeless powder, such as used in artillery cartridges, produces a theoretical exhaust velocity of 10,500 feet per second. Ordinary ethyl alcohol, burned with pure oxygen, has a theoretical exhaust velocity of around 13,700 feet per second. Gasoline, burned with pure oxygen, has one of about 14,500 feet per second, and even aniline burned with nitric acid proves superior to dynamite, with a theoretical exhaust velocity of 11,800 feet per second.

Hudson Maxim, instead of refuting the widespread misunderstanding that "dynamite is more powerful than anything," was talking in terms of money. It would be too expensive to run a car or an airplane on smokeless powder was his main argument.

He emphasized that he was not just calculating costs. "I have conducted more experiments in the use of explosive materials for driving motors than any man living or dead. I have spent more than sixty thousand dollars in these experiments."

His purpose in making all these experiments and in spending all that money was to find a superior system of propulsion for naval torpedoes and, possibly, small torpedo boats. He pointed out that a naval torpedo is in itself an expensive item (the price he quoted was $5,000) and that its purpose is to destroy an even more expensive enemy vessel. "It therefore matters little whether or not the propelling means or motive fluid for the run costs fifty dollars instead of five dollars; but it would make a lot of difference in the economy of running an automobile or an aeroplane."

The main surprise came when I learned in which way Hudson Maxim used his high explosive for driving a naval torpedo. I had best stick to straight quotation now:

"In my system of driving torpedoes, I employ a material called motorite, consisting of seventy per cent nitro-glycerin

and thirty per cent guncotton. In the form in which it is used it is no longer explosive, but burns continuously without explosion.

"Bars of the material seven inches in diameter and five feet long are forced into steel tubes. These tubes are closed at one end and the other end screws into a combustion chamber. Water is forced into the combustion chamber instantly upon ignition of the exposed end of the motorite in the combustion chamber.

"Under three hundred pounds pressure to the square inch, motorite burns at the rate of a foot per minute. The flame blast of the burning motorite atomizes the water by passing with the water through a tube in which baffle plates are placed at intervals. The products of combustion and steam together are utilized to drive a turbine or reciprocating engine, preferably a turbine . . . A pound of motorite will evaporate about two pounds of water, so that each pound of motorite consumed represents three pounds of mixed steam and products of combustion."

Reading this, one wonders how Hudson Maxim managed to miss the "obvious"; if you have a bar of a double-base powder, 7 inches in diameter and 5 feet long, you don't use it to boil water to get steam to drive a turbine, which then drives a propeller. You take your bar of double-base powder and suspend it inside a tube in such a manner that it burns as rapidly as possible and you have a nice solid-fuel missile of reasonable size.

Reading the description of the utilization—provided that's the word to use at this point—of motorite strikes one as a very close miss. One little accident of the right kind would have opened his eyes. The miss is even closer when you read the concluding paragraph, which starts out thus: "I once suggested the use of motorite in small sticks for driving

model aeroplanes in short trial flights. For such use the material would be cheap enough . . ."

I can't resist quoting one more paragraph from the article:

"The cost of driving an engine by means of motorite would be about two dollars per horsepower hour. Therefore, in order to drive a hundred horsepower automobile with motorite it would cost, for fuel alone, two hundred dollars an hour, and the motorite would make a heavy load for the car, as it would require the consumption of nearly a ton of motorite per hour. Therefore, if a hundred horsepower aeroplane were to use motorite for a fuel, it would be unable to carry enough for an hour's flight."

When Hudson Maxim died in 1927, he was seventy-four years old. Conceivably he could have lived for another twenty years. If he had, he would have seen what he missed back in 1910, just because of the accident that didn't happen—and that would have changed history if it had.

4. *The Mystery Plant from Kyrene*

ONCE UPON A TIME there was a plant which Greek-speaking traders called *zilphion*. It may be necessary to point out that the first letter, if the Greek alphabet is used, is a *sigma* which is normally transcribed as an "s" rather than a "z." But all my teachers were in unanimous agreement that the *sigma* was pronounced as a sharp "s" only at the ending of a word and that its sound, if the first letter of a word or name, was likely to be closer to the English "z." That being the case I have decided to spell it the way it is pronounced.

Well, to proceed: if you happen to have a hoard of old coins and among them is one of the two didrachmai pieces from Kyrene (usually spelled Cyrene, but that tends to make it a two-syllable word, originally the place name had three syllables) you not only have a valuable collector's item, you also have a botanical mystery on your hands. For this zilphion plant is the only example of a plant which became extinct within historical times that I know of.

Of animals which became extinct in historical times, we have a deplorably long list, ranging from a case like *Rhytina* (*gigas*) *stelleri,* or Steller's seacow, of which only a few hundred specimens existed when it was discovered, to *Ectopistes migratorius,* the passenger pigeon which in Audubon's times

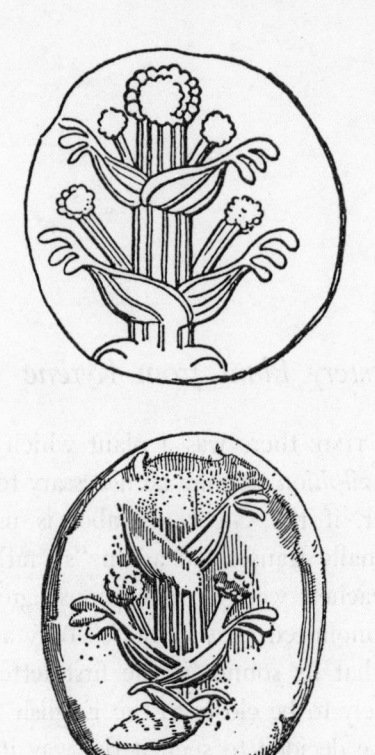

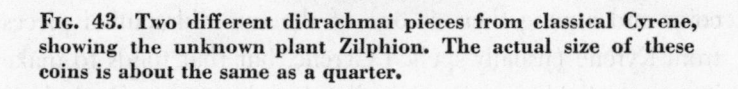

FIG. 43. Two different didrachmai pieces from classical Cyrene, showing the unknown plant Zilphion. The actual size of these coins is about the same as a quarter.

flew over the North American continent in uncountable millions. But nobody ever heard of a plant that flourished in the days of the early civilizations and is now completely unknown—with the exception of this zilphion.

What makes the mystery so astonishing is that zilphion was an article of trade that made several cities rich. The fact alone that it was put on coins indicates that it was valuable, and there existed an idiomatic phrase meaning "more valuable than zilphion." We even have a classical picture of the zil-

phion trade. It is a shallow bowl made around 600 B.C. and found in Italy. Because the main figure in the picture is the ruler Arkesilas III, the bowl is known as the Arkesilas bowl to historians.

The picture shows the king seated under a sun sail, aboard a ship, surrounded by servants who are all carefully labeled. In the ship's bottom, two men stow large bags under the supervision of somebody labeled *phylakos* (overseer), while five men are on deck with the ruler. One is labeled *eirmophoros* (porter), another *isophortos* (in this context, this term is best translated as supervisor) and a third one *zilphiomapsos*, the "zilphion-kneader." And somewhere on the bowl is the exclamation *oryxon* ("Go away!") for reasons unknown to me or anybody else.

As the picture on the oval didrachma shows, the plant had a thick and probably creeping root and a thick stem. Both the Greeks and the Romans liked the young zilphion sprouts as a vegetable, and the stem was eaten too. The taste must have been quite pronounced, because zilphion was used to flavor other dishes. The sap of the stem and the root was condensed into a kind of syrup which had a special Latin name (*laserpitium*) and an easy-to-remember value: If you wanted a pound of laserpitium, you handed over a pound of silver coins.

Zilphion came from North Africa and the people who grew rich ferrying it across the Mediterranean Sea claimed that it could not be cultivated. It grew in certain places in the interior and had to be gathered when in season. Pliny the Elder, in Book V, Chapter 5, of his *Natural History*, stated that "The territory of Cyrene, to a distance of fifteen miles from the shore, is said to abound in trees, while for the same dis-

tance beyond that district it is only suitable for the production of grain: after which a tract of land, thirty miles in breadth and 250 miles in length, is productive of nothing but laser (zilphion)."

Pliny's statement clearly implies that the plant grew wild and was not cultivated. But it was in Pliny's time that zilphion began to disappear. "The zilphion of Cyrene no longer exists," Pliny stated in Book XXII, Chapter 48. But he went on to tell that some came from Syria. Interestingly enough, Pliny speaks about zilphion only as a medicinal plant. Repeated fumigations with the dried root made hemorrhoids disappear. The mashed root, with wine and oil, was good for bruises "and with wax for the cure of scrofulous sores." The leaves, taken with aromatic white wine immediately after a bath, helped women with a dead fetus clear out the uterus—but the concoction was taken internally, in case one wonders how it was supposed to work.

Three centuries after Pliny, the plant zilphion was unknown.

Anybody who wanted to could—and can even now—read the descriptions of the plant as given by Theophrastus, Dioscorides, Columella and other classical writers. It does not help much, even though the descriptions and the pictures on the coins agree nicely. Early in the nineteenth century, French botanists thought that zilphion was probably the plant listed as *Thapsia garganica*, but the German pharmacologist Schroff showed as long ago as 1862 that the classical authors mentioned had described that plant separately. Obviously it was not the same as zilphion.

Another guess was that zilphion might have been a local name for the plant *Ferula asafoetida*. But that one, as its scientific name indicates, has an unpleasant smell, and nobody in his right mind would use it as a flavoring. Besides,

it did not grow in North Africa but farther East, mainly in Persia.

Difficult as it is, we have to accept zilphion as extinct. And we'll never know just what kind of vegetable it made on the tables of well-to-do Greeks of antiquity.

CHAPTER XVI

THE OBSERVATORY ON THE MOON

ON THE LAST DAY OF JULY 1964, spacecraft *Ranger VII*, on its way to the moon, began to take and transmit pictures when it was still 1600 miles from the lunar surface. Its last picture, the 4316th, was taken only 1000 feet from the surface and showed objects just one yard across. Spacecraft *Ranger VIII* followed in February 1965 and transmitted 7137 pictures back to earth. It was followed by *Ranger IX* in March 1965, which transmitted more than 5000 pictures; and *Ranger IX* was followed by the Russian spacecraft *Zond-3* which photographed most of the far side of the moon. *Zond-3*, in turn, was followed by *Luna-9* in February 1966, the first man-made device that succeeded in soft-landing on the lunar surface and transmitting pictures of a tiny section of the moon as it would look to a man sitting on the ground there.

If, by the beginning of 1965, anybody was still skeptical about an actual man standing or sitting on the lunar surface within a few years, any such skepticism has now been dispelled.

But after the first landing on the moon has been accomplished, what is going to follow?

Everybody is agreed on a number of fundamental thoughts, goals and conclusions. Of course the first landing will be followed by others, there will be a base on the moon—or rather a minimum of two, one speaking Russian, the other English—

and there is also agreement that the main purpose of the lunar base will be research: chemistry, crystallography, electronics, metallurgy, biology and last, but by no means least, astronomy.

Building an observatory on the moon will be a curious turnabout. After having done what we could with telescopes, *Ranger* flights, *Surveyor* landings and manned landings to explore the moon, the moon itself will be utilized for further astronomical exploration.

Of course it is difficult to imagine a better location for an astronomical observatory than a place on the lunar surface. Since the atmosphere is negligible (at most of a density of 1/20,000th of ours at sea level) the seeing will be perfect all the time, not only during the two-week night, but also all day long. Only two rather small areas of the sky will not be accessible; namely the area occupied by the sun and its corona and the one occupied by the earth. But any astronomer will know in advance where the sun and the earth are going to be.

Because of the lack of an atmosphere an object just above the horizon can be observed just as well as one near the zenith. And since the moon is a negligible distance from the earth, as cosmic distances go, the fixed stars will be in the customary places, existing charts can, therefore, be used without making any change at all.

To make the picture even more attractive, the moon does not move fast in its orbit (0.6 mile per second) and it needs a whole month to turn on its axis. This means that the apparent motion of fixed stars and of extragalactic objects across the lunar sky is quite slow. Any object can be kept in the field of view for an endless time; we can start dreaming right now about what a 240-hour exposure of the Andromeda galaxy may show.

The longer you look at all the possible advantages the more

it becomes clear that an astronomical observatory on the moon will be something very much worth having. Just for the sake of completeness I would like to add that this is not a new idea to astronomers. The two lunar observers Wilhelm Beer and Heinrich von Mädler who had completed a 3-foot chart of the moon in 1834, published a book explaining the features on their chart in 1837. In that book they *included a short section on the advantages of an astronomical observatory on the moon!* If the first lunar observatory is officially opened in 1977—a reasonable estimate—140 years will have gone by between first dream and reality. During the latter part of these fourteen decades astronomy added to itself another branch, namely radio astronomy, something even Beer and von Mädler did not dream about.

There is a reason for bringing up radio astronomy even before the discussion is really underway. It is because the type of instrument used may determine the choice of locations for the observatory. Beer and von Mädler had said that the lunar observatory should be on the moon's far side, so that earthlight would not interfere. They still thought that the moon had a reasonably dense atmosphere, much less dense than ours, of course, but still dense enough to make the sky light if a strongly luminous body, like the sun or the earth, was overhead. We now know better; what there is of a lunar atmosphere will not produce any optical effects. In fact an observatory using normal telescopes and astronomical cameras should be located on the lunar hemisphere visible from earth for ease in communications.

But when it comes to radio astronomy the earth does interfere; not the planet itself, but the activities of its inhabitants. More and more wave bands have to be utilized for communication of all kinds and the volume of radio transmissions into and from space is bound to increase sharply. Communica-

tions satellites will be in action, weather watching satellites will send a steady stream of information to the ground, navigational satellites will broadcast their position when requested by navigators at sea. There will be all kinds of special devices, manned orbiting laboratories and so forth, in various orbits around the earth, all of them broadcasting and receiving. One worried radio astronomer has already gone on record as saying that his special branch of science will be blotted out a decade from now.

But the other side of the moon is a perfect refuge for radio astronomers, since the bulk of the moon will protect their instruments from all the man-made radio noises so that they will be able to study radio noise coming in from deep space.

Not quite forty years ago somebody in Germany—probably Max Valier, but I am not sure—sold an article on the advantages of a lunar observatory to a German weekly magazine. Since this was an illustrated family magazine the article had to have a picture to go with it and a staff artist was called in to do the job.

The picture showed a magnificently rocky lunar landscape with tall and steep mountains and on one of the mountain tops there was the observatory, with three cupolas of different sizes, and three telescopes showing in the cupola slots, all three looking in the same direction. I'll admit freely that I don't know just what the lunar observatory will look like, but I know it won't look like that illustration.

To begin with it will not be on a mountain top. On earth you build observatories on high mountains to have as much of the troublesome atmosphere as possible below. On the moon the favored site for an observatory would be one where the observer had a clear view down to the horizon in all directions. Since the horizon on the moon is much closer to the

observer than on earth this is not a very difficult demand, the center of any large flat-floored crater will do. To an observer in the center of Archimedes, for example, the horizon would appear unmarred since even the ringwall of the crater itself would be below the horizon.

On earth the cupola has the purpose of protecting the expensive instrument from the elements, rain, hail, snow and sometimes wind-blown dust and sand. On the moon protection is needed from the steady infall of micrometeorites, but it probably won't take the shape of the customary cupola.

When it comes to the instrument itself the layman is apt to visualize something large and impressive, possibly a big reflecting telescope like the 80-inch reflector of the Kitt Peak National Observatory not far from Tucson, or at least a 36-inch refractor like that of the Lick Observatory. The answer to such ideas is a plain "no" and the reason is weight. But it may be useful to explain the two main types of optical telescopes first.

The instrument astronomers call a refractor is a very large spyglass, a tube holding two lenses or rather lens systems. The purpose of the tube is two-fold; it carries the main lens at its outer end and it also keeps out stray light. Since the main lens is heavy the tube carrying it must be very strong and is heavy too, for that reason.

Things are a little bit better in the case of the reflector where the main optical element is a carefully ground mirror. The mirror is located at the lower end of the tube. Since all large modern reflectors are housed in cupolas the tube does not need to keep out stray light and is, therefore, usually a lattice construction and no longer a tube in the proper meaning of the word.

The largest refractor ever built—with one exception that will be discussed below—is the 40-inch refractor of the Yerkes

Observatory, next largest is the 36-inch of the Lick Observatory. The 32.7-inch of the Paris Observatory at Meudon holds third place.

Largest of the reflectors is, of course, the 200-inch on Palomar Mountain, with the 120-inch of Lick Observatory and the 100-inch on Mt. Wilson in second and third places.

The customary question whether a refractor or a reflector is "better" has no short answer; it would be like asking whether a Diesel engine or a gasoline engine is "better." It depends on the job, plus other factors. At the present state of technology we can build 100-inch, 120-inch reflectors, but we could not build refractors with corresponding lens diameters. The point to keep in mind, in general, as well as with specific reference to the lunar observatory, is that a larger telescope does not only produce a larger magnification. The main thing is that a larger lens, or mirror, has a larger light gathering power and can therefore reveal the existence of very faint objects, as for example very distant galaxies. In layman's language this is usually expressed by saying that the bigger telescope can "see farther" which is correct only insofar that a very faint galaxy is likely to be much farther away than a fairly bright galaxy.

The light gathering ability and the resolution (alias magnification) do not increase at the same rate as the diameter of the lens or mirror increases. The resolution increases in proportion to the diameter. Hence the 200-inch reflector on Palomar Mountain has a resolution twice as good as the 100-inch on Mt. Wilson. But the light gathering ability increases with the square of the diameter. Therefore the 200-inch can gather four times as much light as the 100-inch. Hence the targets of the 200-inch, and of the 100-inch too, are usually distant galaxies. For observing Jupiter, which is bright enough, a much smaller instrument is very nearly as good as these giants.

But now I cannot hold back any more on the problem of weight and I feel obliged to give advance warning that things will look quite bleak for a few paragraphs to come.

To begin with a historical example: Lord Rosse's "giant of Parsonstown" a 72-inch reflector, had a total weight of 36,000 pounds. Its tube, made of sturdy wood and strengthened with iron hoops, alone weighed 15,000 pounds. Oh well, that was a century ago. We can build lighter now. Well, maybe we build better, but not lighter. The Kitt Peak 80-inch reflector has an overall weight of 70 tons, without the foundation, that is. Lick's 120-inch is estimated to weigh 40 tons (just the instrument and mounting) while the Palomar 200-inch has a weight of 150 tons, the mirror alone weighs 14½ tons—the glass disk before grinding weighed in at 20 tons.

Nor can any comfort be derived from the weights of the bigger radio telescopes. Harvard's George R. Agassiz radio telescope near Cambridge has a 60-foot dish weighing 8000 pounds (being of extra light construction) but the total weight is 103,600 pounds. The Navy's 84-foot radio telescope of Maryland Point Observatory has a total weight of 170,000 pounds, the dish alone weighs 15,000 pounds. And Great Britain's Jodrell Bank radio telescope is not only the biggest fully steerable radio telescope in existence, it is also exceptionally heavy: the 250-foot dish weighs 750 tons and the whole moveable structure adds up to 2000 tons.

Of course I am well aware of the fact that under the moon's lesser gravity less metal will provide the same structural strength. A radio telescope of the same dimensions as the one at Jodrell Bank might have 350 tons earth weight (and weigh only 60 tons on the moon), but this weight would have to be lifted out of the atmosphere against the earth's gravitational pull and would then have to be soft-landed on the

moon. And while a radio telescope could still be transported in pieces that could be designed with the weight carrying capacity of the then existing rockets in mind, any optical telescope has one piece that has to be transported as a whole: the mirror in the case of a reflector and the main lens in the case of a refractor. And the weight of a mirror or lens could not be reduced very much, even for use on the moon.

Are we then limited to 8-inch and 10-inch telescopes for the lunar observatory? Not necessarily, because at one time in the past a refractor of an even larger size than the 40-inch of Yerkes Observatory was built along unconventional lines. It is usually not mentioned in astronomical books for two reasons: it never did any scientific work and it was dismantled only a few years after it had been built.

It was the 49.2-inch refractor that could be seen at the Paris Universal Exhibition of 1900. At the time the French considered themselves the leading nation in the manufacture of precision optical instruments. Of course when this claim was made Americans tended to mutter "Alvan G. Clark" and Germans said "Carl Zeiss," but these old rivalries are by now a thing of the past. At any event the *Palais de l'Optique* at the Paris Exhibition was to have a very large telescope. Since the biggest instrument up to that time had been Lord Rosse's reflector—inactive since 1878—a three-meter (circa 110-inch) reflector was considered first, but facilities for casting a glass disk of such size simply did not exist, not in France and not anywhere else on our planet. But an 80-inch disk for a mirror could be cast, and a 50-inch disk for a lens.

These two facilities were combined for the 49.2-inch refractor. Since the main lens was expected to weigh close to a ton no attempts at normal mounting were made. The lens was mounted at the front end of a 190-foot steel tube which was resting on the ground horizontally. The eye piece and plate

holders for photographic plates, 30-inches square, were in a small wheeled cart connected to the steel tube by bellows like those of an oversized camera. For focussing purposes this cart could be moved as much as five feet, its wheel resting on a short section of narrow gauge railroad track. In order to reflect starlight into the telescope a 12-inch thick plane mirror, with a diameter of 79 inches, was set into a vertical fork mounting.

The disappointing performance of the instrument was not due to poor optics but had other reasons. No provision had been made for ventilating the steel tube properly so that the air inside the tube was probably quite humid. But the main reason was the location of the instrument; from the point of view of the observing astronomer it was undoubtedly the worst location possible. It was not many feet above sea level, on fair grounds where hundreds of searchlights were operated on and off, and near a very large city which must have been much smokier in 1900 than it is now.

Still, this type of telescope might be the thing to use on the moon. The heaviest part that would have to be transported would be the main lens, and if we have a 30-inch lens in mind that means a weight (uncrated) of around 750 pounds. The plane mirror for reflecting starlight into the telescope could be much lighter than the one used in 1900 and would weigh less than the main lens. Instead of using a horizontal 30-inch steel tube one could drill a horizontal, or even slanting, 30-inch tube through a convenient rock formation. Housing the eye piece and photographic equipment in a separate car would solve the problem of breathing for the observer. With any conventional telescope one would have the problem of either enclosing the whole telescope in an underground room with breathable air, or else exposing the whole telescope to the vacuum of the lunar surface and hav-

ing the observer in a spacesuit. Neither sounds like an optimal solution, but if a telescope of that type were used, the tunnel in the rock could be a vacuum while the observers are in their enclosed cabin with an airlock to the interior of the lunar base.

Direct observation, which was the rule in the past, is now pretty much the exception and used mainly for work on other planets. Practically everything else is photographic work and if an astronomical camera is used, it can well be operated by a man in a spacesuit since his main jobs would be to aim the camera and to change plates. And astronomical cameras, fortunately, are much lighter than astronomical telescopes. Harvard's "Super Schmidt" meteor camera at Las Cruces is an 18-inch camera with a total weight of 5000 pounds. Redesigning such a camera for use on the moon could eliminate a good percentage of this weight, possibly as much as 50 per cent. It must also be kept in mind that so far nobody had *tried* to design light large scale astronomical equipment, all the efforts to eliminate weight have gone into small portable telescopes.

But how about reflectors with a lightweight mirror? The mirror does not have to be glass, as is the case with the 200-inch and its smaller rivals. The reason why instrument makers went from Sir William Herschel's speculum metal mirrors to glass mirrors which were silvered (and later aluminized) was purely practical. The chemical action of the atmosphere slowly reduces the reflectivity of the mirror. Partly it is straight oxidation, partly the action of gases which are not frequent in the atmosphere, but often present, for example sulphur dioxide that is released not only by industry but by volcanoes, too. If a speculum metal mirror grew dim, it meant repolishing, which is at the very least tedious work. If a silvered or aluminized glass mirror grows dim, the glass disk

is simply resilvered. But on the moon there is no atmosphere which causes trouble via unwanted chemical reactions.

Could we produce an all aluminum mirror of little weight and with a diameter of, say, 50 inches? Of course lightweight parabolic mirrors of a diameter of 4 to 6 feet exist for various purposes, but they are not accurate enough for astronomical use. Again since no work in this direction has been carried out, we don't know whether it can be done or not. It would be a development project which might not even be very expensive.

Before we look at the back side of the moon and the radio telescope station we might think quickly about a likely location for the visual observatory. My own suggestion is the large half crater with the beautiful name of *Sinus iridum* (Bay of Rainbows) at the northern edge of the *Mare imbrium*. There the horizon would be as smooth as it is on earth a hundred miles from the nearest shoreline at sea. Moreover, the ground would not get too hot. Most people "know" that the noonday temperature on the moon is near the boiling point of water. This information is correct, but it holds true only near the lunar equator. In the area of *Sinus iridum* the noonday temperature of the ground will be around 80° Fahrenheit. The night temperature will be as low as anywhere else, an estimated 200° Fahrenheit below zero, but at least the daytime temperatures do not climb as high as they do at the equator.

An observatory in the center of the *Sinus iridum* would have a location which would correspond more or less to an observatory near Paris or Vienna as far as the astronomical view is concerned. It would be excellent for the northern stars, but would not do so well for the southern stars. The lunar equivalent of a Cape Town Observatory would be located in Cla-

vius. It looks as if we had a choice between two observatories in two different locations or of braving the daytime heat of the equator, which would not be too difficult to beat by digging in. But two observatories seem to be a better answer just because of the work-load that will indubitably descend on them. Instrument time is tightly apportioned in terrestrial observatories, and trying to observe the whole sky from just one observatory is likely to demand the impossible.

Let us now consider the radio telescope on the far side of the moon. Like its optical counterpart it should be well away from the lunar equator and for the same reason. And as for its construction we have a "prototype" on earth right now: the Arecibo radio telescope which has the largest antenna dish of all, namely 1000 feet in diameter, and weighs less per square foot than any other radio telescope, mainly because it is also, in a manner of speaking, lying flat on the ground.

In its construction a natural hollow in the ground was utilized. It was not "lined with wire mesh" as one can read occasionally, but the wire mesh was suspended across the hollow in such a manner that it has the proper curved surface. The wire mesh is supported by cables to which ballast bars are tied. The ballast bars, by their weight, change the curve which a suspended cable would form naturally into a segment of a sphere.

For those who are surprised at the mention of wire mesh for the "reflector" I hasten to explain that a reflector for radio waves does not have to be a continuous surface, even though some of the smaller dishes have been made of sheet metal. It is all a question of the wavelength you are dealing with. The reflecting mirror of an optical telescope would still be optically perfect, even if it had millions of tiny holes, provided that the size of each hole is less than 1/20th of the wavelength reflected. Since the waves of visible light are so short, this is

only a point of theoretical information. But if you deal with 20 centimeter (circa 8 inch) radio waves, holes of 1 centimeter in diameter are permissible, hence wire mesh can be used. Theoretically the spaces between the wires in the Arecibo telescope would have to be smaller than 5 centimeters and the deviation of the shape of the net has the same limit. For the radio waves to be received this is a "smooth" mirror. In reality the spacing of the wires at Arecibo is only 1.3 centimeters and the error in shape is at most 2.5 centimeters.

Incidentally the Arecibo telescope can be operated as a pure radio telescope, just receiving waves that come from space, or else it can be operated as a radar telescope, sending out pulses of radio waves and catching their reflections. The structure where the radio waves are received and the radar impulses are transmitted is suspended on cables 472 feet above the large bowl. Of course a radio telescope of this type is not as versatile as the fully steerable Jodrell Bank equipment, but for weight reasons the radio telescope on the moon will have to be of that type.

One more problem needs to be discussed.

The distance between the two observatories is likely to be on the order of 2000 miles. They have to communicate with each other and possibly also with some research outposts in other distant areas of the moon. The most practicable and also the cheapest way of doing it will be by moon-orbiting communications satellite. But because the moon's gravitational field is weak, a moon-orbiting satellite travels slowly. A satellite needing two hours to complete one orbit would be 1075 miles above sea level in the case of the earth, the two-hour orbit for the moon is only 90 miles above its surface. And because of the moon's curvature it will be visible only along a rather narrow lane on the ground. It would help a little if the

communications satellite were placed in a polar orbit. But a much larger orbit (see Fig. 44) would be preferable.

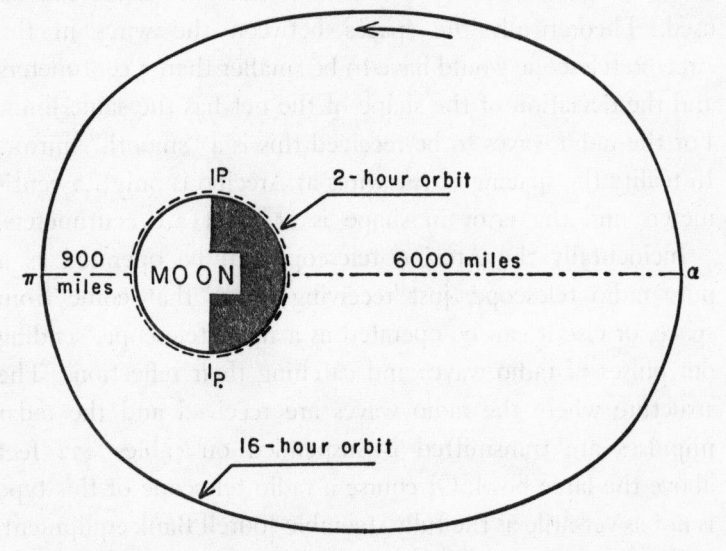

FIG. 44. Two possible orbits for communication satellites around the moon.

A communications satellite in a 16-hour orbit would be visible, and therefore useable, for several hours at a time—if it is visible from both observatories simultaneously there could be "live" communication. Otherwise storage tapes would have to be used.

But a satellite in such an orbit would move much faster in the "periselenion" (closest to the moon) sector of its orbit than in the opposite, the "aposelenion" sector. This fact can be utilized in the following manner: the orbit of the communications satellite could be tilted in such a way that aposelenion is vertically above the half way point of the line connecting the two observatories. In that case the communications satellite would be above the horizon for both observatories for

about 10 hours and would be below the horizon for one of them, or both, for only 6 hours.

The astronomical observatory on the moon about which Beer and von Mädler dreamed more than a century ago will become reality long before the current century draws to a close. But it will look quite differently from the terrestrial shape these two observers probably had in mind.

OBSERVATORY ON THE MOON
by Donald H. Menzel

My good friend, Willy Ley, has pointed out the usefulness of a manned observatory on the surface of the moon. We agree completely on the excellence of a lunar site, with clear, black skies by day as well as by night. The stars stand steady and untwinkling in this airless, waterless world.

I do not agree with Willy Ley, however, concerning the types of telescopes to be used in this observatory, the operation of such telescopes, their location on the surface of the moon, or the specific programs that one would use the instruments for.

First of all, with reference to the location of a radio telescope, I am not altogether convinced that the best location would be on the far side of the moon. True, such a location would be free from man-made radio noise of terrestrial origin. But this is not likely to be particularly troublesome. One must not overlook the advantages of direct communication from earth to moon that would result from an observatory located on the side turned toward the earth. In any event, we must weigh the disadvantages of having the earth available to help us in certain radio experiments. Today astronomers

find the moon a big help, as it moves over this or that radio source, hiding it from view. The earth could be similarly used for a moon-based telescope. It could give us important information, for example, about the spatial distribution of radio sources on the sun or within the solar atmosphere, during those times when the earth eclipses the sun.

In my opinion, the advantages of an optical observatory on the moon are even more spectacular than those for radio astronomy. Here, Willy Ley and I concur that the observatory should be located on the earthward hemisphere.

The moon's orbital velocity is irrelevant. We correct for the moon's rotation, slow though it is, by means of telescopic controls similiar to those on earth. True, the long lunar day (or night), lasting 14 earthly days, would permit long exposures on certain faint objects. But the most obvious advantage to a moon-based observatory would be our ability to study the structure of the universe in light of the wavelengths that fail to penetrate the earth's atmosphere, light or energy that we would describe as far ultraviolet, or even X-rays. For such a purpose man clearly needs a reflecting telescope, not a refractor. Glass absorbs the ultraviolet light—hence no one would ever consider building a major refractor, as Willy Ley suggests.

I disagree completely when he states that today we cannot build lighter telescopes, even though we may build better ones. The basic problem is not the gravitational field of the earth, although that enters indirectly, but the gravitational field of the moon where the instrument ultimately has to operate. We have built mirrors that are much lighter than the solid glass mirrors used for the Palomar giant. A relatively thin layer of quartz melted on top of a much thicker, but stable, layer of foamed quartz gives a very rigid mirror. The weight of the

mirror is a small part of the weight of the telescope as a whole. We could most certainly send to the moon a 100-inch mirror or larger. But in the low gravitational field of the moon, the mirror and its supporting telescope will be subject to only one-sixth of the gravitational field of the earth. Distortions will be correspondingly less and easier to control. The telescope can be much lighter in consequence.

Willy Ley seems to be concerned that the astronomer might experience difficulties operating in a vacuum. As a matter of fact, electronic receivers would carry the image from the telescope itself to underground, pressured chambers where the observer could operate in comfort. Remote control would enable him to perform all of the necessary telescope operations. In this way, we should have the enormous advantage of high resolution of a large telescope, in addition to its light-gathering power.

I might mention here that the telescope I have described could not possibly function for X-ray astronomy. The X-ray telescope would look something like a giant insect's eye, an enormous honeycomb of tiny cells turning around in space to measure the intensities of cosmic X-rays coming from different directions of space. Electronic detectors would record the information. Such detectors have already been sent up into space by Dr. Herbert Friedman and his collaborators at the U. S. Naval laboratory. There they have detected X-rays emitted by various kinds of astronomical bodies. Such studies are extremely important.

Willy Ley suggests that temperature considerations would indicate a preference for the location of either a radio or optical observatory at some distance from the lunar equator. The temperature of the equipment would, beyond doubt, get pretty high near the equator, if the instrument were not

shielded in some way or other. I think that a very simple screen could be devised to put the instrument completely in shadow, to protect it from the sun's rays. Alternatively, one could certainly cool the instrument by circulating some fluid through it, as we do today in many industrial plants.

However, if one decides to move away from the equator, for one reason or another I should most certainly recommend that the first lunar telescope be placed in the southern hemisphere, not in the northern. This is because the most interesting and significant part of our stellar universe, which such a telescope would study, lies in the southern hemisphere. Certainly *Sinus Iridum* would be a good location for the *second* moon-based optical telescope.

I question very much whether the first lunar radio telescope should resemble in any way the Arecibo horizontal dish. The low gravity of the moon should make particularly desirable the construction of at least a partially steerable dish and that is what I would most certainly recommend. In any event, such a permanent dish, located far from the equator, would not be able to study the sun or the planets of the solar system. Indeed, the choice of Arecibo, Puerto Rico, as the site for the big dish was largely dictated by astronomical considerations.

Finally, I should most certainly recommend that, if a radio telescope is to be built on the moon, it be located close to the optical telescope. I mention this not only to simplify the communication system, whose complexity Willy Ley elaborates, but to simplify the whole problem of logistics of a moon-based scientific station.

However, despite our disagreement on details, Willy Ley and I agree completely that such an observatory will become an eventuality within the next three or four decades. I wish, moreover, to emphasize the knowledge to be gained from such

an observatory and associated scientific programs will contribute greatly to our understanding of the origin and ultimate destiny of our universe.

AN EYE FOR SELENE
by Robert S. Richardson

There is one aspect to this business of putting an observatory on the Moon that has me worried. What are the astronomers on Luna going to use as a subject for conversation?

Astronomers are not the sort of people who have a large fund of small talk. They consist mostly of grim, taciturn individuals with a gloomy outlook on life. Conversation often languishes when they gather around the dinner table at their mountaintop observatory. But there is one subject that always interests them: *What is the seeing?*

The seeing, of course, refers to the appearance of the image in the telescope as affected by atmospheric conditions. If the seeing is bad they grumble about their luck and swear that somebody up there hates them. If the seeing is good they perk up momentarily. Now on the Moon they will always have "Seeing 10"—perfect! In fact, there won't really be any seeing. What a horrible situation. A bunch of astronomers with nothing to complain about!

It is impossible for a person without telescopic experience to appreciate the extent that astronomers are handicapped by the atmosphere. A physicist or chemist works in the laboratory where conditions are under their control. But an astronomer is completely at the mercy of his environment.

It is not just a clear sky that he needs. After a storm the

sky may be crystal clear. But the air is so turbulent the stars are twinkling like mad. Which means that in the telescope they will be jumping all over the place. Sometimes a star will explode right in your eye! And the bigger the telescope the more adversely is it affected by seeing. There are scarcely two dozen nights in the year when a telescope like the 200-inch Hale can approach the full extent of its optical power. (Curiously enough the seeing is usually improved by smoke and haze. Possibly the smoke particles reduce turbulence by loading the atmosphere. E. E. Barnard said the best view of Venus he ever had was when the sky over the Lick Observatory was brown from a forest fire.)

Even on those all too rare nights when the seeing is good the atmosphere is still an obstacle. For it prevents about 30 per cent of the light of a star from reaching the telescope. Worse still . . . this is the 30 per cent that contains some of the most valuable information about the sun and stars. Beginning in the ultraviolet at wavelength 3200A, the spectrum begins to weaken and at 2950A is gone completely, due to absorption in the ozonosphere. Further absorption due to molecules and atoms of oxygen and nitrogen continues into the X-ray region. Only recently has this "rocket ultraviolet" region become accessible to exploration.

But on the airless surface of the Moon we would get *all* the radiation of the celestial bodies. The stars would be hard unwinking points of light set in a sky never stained by clouds.

Exposure times on stellar spectra should be drastically reduced. When the seeing is bad the image of your star is dancing around on the polished face of the slit *jaws* instead of going into the *slit* where you want it. Direct photography will also be benefited. The light in a star image will be con-

centrated in a tiny point on the emulsion instead of being spread over an area to form a spot.

For work on the Moon the best type of optical telescope would seem to be the reflector, as the reflector or mirror type of telescope can be made so much larger than the refractor or lens type. Also, the reflector is such a versatile sort of instrument compared with the refractor. Furthermore, a refractor would bring you right back to all the disadvantages of observing through the atmosphere in the violet and ultraviolet, since glass begins to absorb strongly around 3400A. All work in the ultraviolet has to be done with mirror systems and concave grating spectrographs.

The trouble with a refractor is that you can't do anything but *look* through it. But astronomers never look into a telescope any more except to focus it and make sure they're set on the right object. There are very few astronomers today who are experienced visual observers, of the caliber of such greats as Schiaparelli and Antoniadi and Lowell. The only ones I can think of at the moment are Clyde Tombaugh, the discoverer of Pluto, and Audouin Dollfus of the Meudon Observatory.

LOCATION OF THE LUNAR BASE

At least six different people have picked out as many different sites for the lunar base. The most extensive investigation on this important problem has been made by John W. Salisbury and Charles F. Campen, Jr., of the Air Force Cambridge Research Laboratories. (AFCRL 870, GRD Research Notes No. 70, Project 7698, October, 1961.) After a review of all the material they recommend that "location of the lunar base in the highlands would be permissible because the discontinuous layers of the rubble, rock

flour and meteoric material overlying the fractured basement
rock would not present a collapse hazard. The maria, on the
other hand, are considered to bear near-surface cavities probably twice the size of those predicted under the volcanic
theory. This added collapse hazard, when compared to the
negligible collapse hazard of the highlands, makes the highlands a more favorable site for base location, and such a site
is advocated in this report." In particular ". . . considering
the probable lunar structure, surface characteristics and natural resources, it appears that the lunar base should be located in the highlands near a rille, but not near a recent
large crater such as Copernicus or Kepler. Also, bearing in
mind astronomical, guidance and propulsion requirements,
for a base near the equator and in the center of the lunar
face, a location in the highlands just south of the Hyginus
Rille, near the crater Agrippa (8° E long., 5° N lat.), is
provisionally proposed for the lunar base."

THE ASTRONOMICAL OBSERVATORIES

When it comes to making astronomical observations on
the Moon we are reminded of the famous statement Lincoln
made about establishing confidence with the public. At one
of the poles of the Moon you can observe half the stars all
of the time; at the lunar equator you can observe all of the
stars half of the time; but there is no place on the Moon
where you can observe all of the stars all of the time. One
thing we can say: it is absolutely essential to have two lunar
observatories located 180° apart.

As seen from the north pole of the Moon the stars would
appear to move in circles around a point in the zenith near
the faint star 36 Draconis, which for want of a better object
will have to serve as the North Star of the Moon. For the

north polar observatory the astronomers would never be able to study stars south of the ecliptic such as Sirius, Antares or Rigel. At the south lunar pole the stars would circle around a point at the zenith near the 4th magnitude star Delta Mensae. The South Star would probably be Canopus, the next brightest star to Sirius, although it is about 15° from the south celestial pole. From the south's polar observatory the astronomers would never be able to study stars north of the ecliptic such as Capella, Vega or Arcturus. From either observatory the Sun, Earth and planets would always be near the horizon and only visible intermittently.

If the two observatories were located 180° apart along the lunar equator, each would see half the celestial sphere at any instant. As on the Earth, the stars would rise in the east and set in the west, only their diurnal motion would be much slower, the Moon requiring 27.32 days to make a complete rotation relative to the stars. The Earth, Sun and planets would pass close to the zenith. The Sun would move even more deliberately than the stars, taking nearly 15 days to pass across the sky and set below the western horizon. To a casual observer the Earth would be a huge bluish globe hanging nearly motionless in the sky, although careful observation would show that it swings through an angle of about 8° to the east and to the west, and over a total distance of about 13° in a north-south direction.

Although the Earth would scarcely seem to move relative to the lunar landscape, a few hours' watching would reveal that it is moving fairly rapidly relative to the stars, passing over an angular distance equal to its width in 4 hours. This apparent motion of the Earth, of course, is due to the revolution of the Moon around it.

If for some reason it is desirable to have the Earth in view of both observatories at all times they should be lo-

cated on the equator between longitudes 82° E and 82° W. But it would probably be advantageous to have a radio telescope located on the far side of the Moon, where it would be shielded from man-made interference.

THE CHANGING STARS

The position of a star on the celestial sphere is designated by its right ascension and declination. The right ascensions and declinations of the stars change continually owing to a conical motion of the Earth's axis in space called precession. The direction of the north celestial pole is not fixed but describes a circle of 23°.5 in radius in a period of 26,000 years. Right now the north celestial pole is near Alpha Ursae Minoris, the star at the end of the handle of the Little Dipper. But by A.D. 7500 the direction of the north pole will have shifted so that Alpha Cephei will be our Polaris, and around A.D. 14,000 this distinction will fall to the bright star Vega. This precessional motion of the Earth is so slow that it only needs to be taken into account in rather precise work. If you wanted to set on a star tonight, and you only had its position for 1940, you could probably find it without bothering to bring its right ascension and declination up to date.

But not on the Moon you couldn't. The axis of the Moon also describes a circle in space with a radius of only 1°.5, instead of 23°.5 as in the case of the Earth. But the lunar axis precesses much faster, making a revolution in 18½ years instead of 26,000 years. As a result, lunar right ascensions would change at a terrific rate. There would be no trouble in calculating them as the problem is thoroughly understood. It would just mean a little more work for the staff at the Naval Observatory.

A lunar astronomical observatory has a tremendous potential. We have only touched upon a few of its major advantages. Now if the lunar astronomers can just find something to talk about . . .